A Kid off the Bank

C. S. SIDAWAY

Published by Sidaway Publications 2020

A Kid off the Bank
by Colin Sidaway

© Colin Sidaway 2020

A catalogue card for this book is available from the British Library.

Paperback ISBN: 978-1-9163934-2-4
Ebook ISBN: 978-1-9163934-3-1
First published in 2020

Publication support

TJ INK
tjink.co.uk

PH MEDIA
phmedia.com

Printed and bound in Great Britain by
TJ International, Padstow, Cornwall

DEDICATION

I would like to dedicate this book to my friend of many years,
Jack Haddock. He died in 2003 having lived in Walsall all his life
and if it was a bus, a train or a canal boat, he photographed it.
All his collection of slides are now in the Walsall Archive.

Dr Colin S. Sidaway
Author and Publisher
May 2020

Birchills Power Station Walsall

CHAPTER ONE

It was one of those days. Nothing to do and nowhere to go but look after my 10 year old son while my wife, his mother, was serving tea and biscuits at a Woman's Institute fund raising event. I thought that a trip down memory lane was called for. It had been close on 20 years since I first put my feet on the canal towpath and this was a good time as any to do it.

I now lived in a leafy suburb of Walsall, there were other parts not so leafy where we had our factory but this was my wife's choice. I didn't really care where I lived as long as there was a good pub within walking distance but today I decided that there were a few places I needed to revisit.

Ruth, my wife, was full of instructions about what I was to do while she was busy selling the cakes she had baked. There were enough cakes to feed a regiment. Oliver was allowed one. I wasn't. Oliver is the name of my son, not my choice but evidently it was a family name on Ruth's side of the family. I found a duffel jacket and bundled Oliver into my Morris Oxford to drive to the other side of town; the not so leafy part.

I pulled off the road at Green Lane. I was aware that the Walsall trolley buses not only had a good turn of speed but you never heard them coming until there was a flash of Royal Blue and it had passed you. I took Oliver by the hand and crossed the road and looked over the

Green Lane Canal Bridge. At the age of 10, I wondered how much longer I would be able to hold his hand as we crossed the road. I guessed that pretty soon now he would be exerting his independence.

It was late Saturday morning and I half expected to see some boats moving, well at least one but there was nothing. I looked out over Birchills Junction all the wharves on the offside were now completely covered in undergrowth. I was going to say weeds but some weeds are bigger than others and bull rushes were very large weeds. The Wyrley and Essington Canal wound its silent way to Sneyd and Wolverhampton. I recalled that before the war I would have seen at least a boat every two or three minutes. Now there was nothing.

Turning to look around at the chimney stacks and cooling towers of Birchills Power Station, I could see that they were still belching forth smoke and water vapour but there were no coal boats supplying fuel. It all now came by rail. Hmm. That really was a sign of the times.

I crossed over the road and looked in the other direction towards Pratt's Bridge. The name plate on the bridge said Pigot's Bridge but the company Pratt's had a flour mill there and that's what I knew it as. Many were the times when I had delivered flour to the mill. The mill was no longer there. Evidently it was burnt down. All the fire appliances in Walsall attended. The flour mill was rat invested and their behaviour was typical but this was not the sinking of a ship but a burning building. They were seen to be jumping from the burning mill to a watery grave, namely the canal. There were so many that it became like a floating carpet of dead carcases. I bet that was a sight not to behold.

Along the length on the offside were sunken boats. Not just one or two but along the whole length of the canal sometimes two abreast before Worsey's Boat Yard was reached. There were more than a few boats there and I wondered how long Joe Worsey would keep his boat building business going. I thought that there were more boats sunken than were floating. It was a dismal and depressing picture.

I made our way on to the towpath. Beneath Green Lane Bridge was a lengthy narrow section. Passing boats were halted by what was known as strapping that was nothing more than winding a rope around a bollard or stump. The Toll Keeper would come out of his office and gauge the boat, fill out the boatman's ticket before the boat moved on to the next gauging station at Sneyd. There was no longer a Toll Keeper or his little office. I guessed the local kids had pulled it down and thrown the bricks in the cut as was their want.

I felt a tugging at my sleeve. 'Dad, what are you looking at?'

'Nothing in particular. A long time ago I walked along that towpath and also steered a butty.'

'What's a butty? Is that a sort of sandwich with jam or something like that?'

'It wasn't that sort of butty. It was a boat. The canal folk gave them that name. It means friend or mate. The boat had no engine and was pulled along by a horse or another boat with an engine, so the one became a partner or friend to the other.'

'Why didn't the butty have an engine?'

I looked down at my son. At least he was showing an interest.

'Before engines were invented all the boats were drawn along by horses. That's why there's a towpath alongside each and every canal. When diesel engines were fitted to boats they could easily pull a horse drawn boat as well which meant that the captain could double the amount of cargo and get twice the wage.'

'Dad, why were you steering the butty? You never told me that you worked on the canal.'

'No, son, I didn't. If you want to know, I'll tell you while we take a walk to the Walsall Public Wharf.'

Green Lane Bridge and Canal Toll Stop

*Gifford at Green Lane, Walsall (Len Wilson in the hatch,
Bill Woolley and his horse 'Bill' on the towpath)*

CHAPTER TWO

I was happy to relate my story to Oliver. I had no idea how much it would need to be censored. The boating fraternity were verbal to say the least using choice language that was not for the ears of a 10 year old or so I thought. I would have to see how my story evolved. We walked on the towpath along the Walsall Branch Canal holding Oliver's hand as I started my story.

'When I was fifteen, my Dad, your Granddad, thought that I needed to be toughened up. I had passed the entrance exam to the Walsall Grammar School. It was easy to pass when your father paid them.'

'What did Granddad do?'

'He took over the leather factory that his grandfather started way back when. He wanted me first to be a scholar so I went to the Grammar School but he thought for some reason that it was all too easy and I needed to be made of sterner stuff.'

'How did he manage that?'

'It's all part of the story.' I said as I went back to my narrative.

At school, we all learnt Latin and French as well as doing maths and English. We read all sorts of things, classical stuff like, Shakespeare and Longfellow and Dickens. It was all really boring. We also played cricket in the summer months and rugby in the winter. Cricket was alright but I didn't like rugby much. We also had homework so that I would become better educated.

Being better educated in the academic sense is all very well if you are going off to be a teacher or a lawyer or a doctor but I was destined to take over the running of the family business. I needed to have an understanding of people and what a hard day's work was like. In that sense I had little or no idea as all the boys I rubbed shoulders with were all from middle class backgrounds and all had lardy-dah accents so that nobody would connect them with being from the Black Country. They wanted to be seen as above the common man but it was those common men and women that worked for them that kept them in the position they aspired to. It was a boys' only school so I never met any girls or knew any.

One day, my dad was down at the Public Wharf arranging for a cargo of leather to be delivered when he met up with a boating family. Now dad knew that the boatmen had a hard life. They travelled the canal system day in, day out, long hours and little pay. They also had to deal with other boatmen and every day triumphs and disasters.

The man he was talking to was called Len Watson. He was married and had a teenage daughter. He had once worked for the Shropshire Union Canal Company who used to have an office and depot in Walsall on the Public Wharf. Len explained that his journeys were mainly up and down the Shroppie to Ellesmere Port and back carrying a variety of goods. The pay wasn't good. He had always had a horse drawn boat. It had been a family tradition. He had been born on the canal, as had his father and horses and boats were his way of life. But and there always seems to be a 'but', the Company wanted bigger pay loads and more reliable times not depending upon a horse throwing a shoe. They had given him a motor boat with a Bolinder diesel engine. He could use that to tow his butty and there was another 'but'. Since it was just him, his wife, Martha and their 14 year old daughter, Sarah-Anne, to work two boats it was an almost an impossibility for him to continue.

Dad saw this as an opportunity to give me an education in hard work and to make me tougher and have a greater understanding of what it was like being poor and having to work all hours God sends just to put food on the table. A deal was struck. At the end of the school year, I would be sent to work for Mr Watson. He would look after me and dad would pay him for my upkeep. A time limit was put on the arrangement. I was coming up to 16 and at 21 dad wanted me working in the family business learning the trade. So the time scale was set for 5 years. They shook hands on the deal. I didn't find this out until my last week at school.

Dad hadn't told mother about this arrangement either and not only did it come as a shock but there was an almighty row that ensued. Mother wanted me to stay at home. I guess that's what every mother wants for their only son. Being an only child only made things worse. Father was strict. It was almost a carry over from Victorian times when a man's word had to be obeyed. There was no demonstration of affection. I didn't have any recollection of my father ever holding my hand. He had decided. Mother was unhappy at the arrangement and I had no say in the matter.

I left school with a certificate which was more like an annual report. I 'could have done better' was all that I managed. I didn't excel in anything. I was just run of the mill pupil fodder to keep the school image alive and well in the town. There was no leaving party just cheerio to my fellow classmates. I went home wondering what I needed to take with me. I needn't have concerned myself, mother sorted everything out which was mainly clothes to keep me warm and dry.

I remember that first Saturday morning well. I had finished school on Friday and had a small bag of clothes with me as we set off in dad's new car, an Austin 12. It was large and was part of dad's image as being 'The Boss'. I just had the clothes I stood up in. The school uniform had gone. I had a large overcoat and a cap should I ever get cold and or wet and a new pair of boots, not shoes but boots. We met up with Mr Watson.

Dad and Mr Watson went into a discussion. It was dad handing over money not to me but to Mr Watson. He just walked away to the car and drove off leaving me on the wharf with Mr Watson.

Mr Watson turned looking me over. 'You will call me, Mr Watson and my wife, Mrs Watson. Is that clear? You will have the back cabin on the motor. I will live on the butty with Mrs Watson and my daughter, Sarah-Anne in the front cabin. You keep your hands off her, do you hear? There'll be no messing around. I expect you to do a day's work. No work and you won't be fed. Have you got that?'

He was laying down the law as he saw it. I was completely depressed. I would have this for the next five years. I just nodded my head. 'Yes, Mr Watson.'

I was struck by the difference between Mr Watson and my father. Both were of a similar age and were authoritarian but that's where the similarity ended. My father was middle aged and portly having had too many Rotary lunches with little or no exercise. He was also red in the face and a receding hair line. What hair he did have was well glued down with Brylcream. On the other hand Mr Watson was a tall wiry man with a weathered complexion having a thick head of jet black hair. While working on the boats he always wore a trilby.

I walked alongside him as we made our way along the wharf to where his two boats were tied up. They were still in the Shropshire Union Colours of bright scarlet with white lettering. The motor was called *John Peel* and the butty *Rosemary*. The butty was tied up alongside the towpath with the tiller pointing upwards while the motor boat was tied alongside but on the outside. They were both ready to move off. I found out later that when the long curved butty tiller was in that position it gave notice to all other boatmen that the boats were not likely to be moving any time soon. All that was for the future I was now facing what was going to be my home for the next five years. I was depressed.

Mrs Watson was a lovely person. She had dark hair with grey strands appearing. She gave me a warm smile by way of a greeting.

'Hello, son. What's your name? Len never told me.'

'Josh, Mrs Watson, Josh Woodward.'

'I'll just call you Josh whenever I need to. Now come on board and step over on to *Rosemary* and leave your things in the *John Peel* cabin. Len wants to move off with no more messing around, as he calls it.'

I tentatively stepped on to the gunnel and then across the well on the rear of *Rosemary* to get on to the counter of *John Peel*. The cabin doors were already open and I looked inside. It was a traditional boatman's cabin but completely devoid of any decoration or equipment. There was just a coal stove and another door for want of a better description opening

Pair of Traditional Narrow Boats

out on to the engine room that housed the single cylinder Bolinder engine. Mr Watson was already there lighting a blow lamp that was directed to the top of the engine. I wondered if he was trying to set fire to it. I later found out that the cylinder head of the single cylinder Bolinder engine needed to be heated up for at least 20 minutes before it would start. As instructed I left my bag on the side bench and looked out across the canal.

'What are you looking at?'

It was Sarah-Anne pushing me out of the way as she climbed out of the back cabin of the *John Peel*.

'Nothing. I was just looking.'

'We have a name for people off the bank who just look vacantly in to the distance. We call them gongoozlers. It looks as if we have a gongoozler for crew. Have you ever been on the cut before?'

'The cut? No, never.'

'We need help not a gawper and I can see that you won't be any use. I don't know what dad was thinking to take you on.'

'I think its money. My father is paying for my upkeep and Mr Watson is getting a crew for nothing.'

She just gave me a hard look and in one movement stepped from the motor over the butty on to the towpath.

'Don't just stand there gawping. Come and help me untie the boats.'

I clambered over the butty and jumped on to the towpath. Sarah-Anne was already undoing the mooring rope at the front of the boats. I looked at the rope that secured the stern of *Rosemary* and couldn't work out how it had been tied up. Sarah-Anne put the front securing rope on the roof of the fore end cabin of the *Rosemary* before she came to help me. The boat was secured to an iron ring on the edge of the towpath. She climbed on the boat, released it from the T pin on the gunnel and threw the rope off the boat on to the towpath. She then reigned in the unsecured rope, coiling it up and put it on the cabin roof. I was still standing on the towpath.

Mrs Watson was on the front of the motor releasing the butty while Mr Watson was on the counter stern of the *John Peel* putting the engine into a forward motion. The motor eased off alongside the butty with Sarah-Anne securing the tiller. Mrs Watson was standing on the fore end of the butty. As Mr Watson pulled alongside the front of the butty he was handed a rope and Mrs Watson stepped on to the gunnel of the motor. The butty moved away from the bank and the boats were underway while I stood on the towpath.

Sarah-Anne shouted at me. "What are you doing on the towpath? You will have to go and find the turnover bridge and then come back to the locks.'

I had no idea what she was talking about. Mr Watson was concerned with securing the butty while Mrs Watson steered the motor and Sarah-Anne steered the butty away from the bank; so much for my first boat trip.

I turned away from them and walked along the towpath away from the Public Wharf. It was some way to the first bridge across the canal. On top of the bridge I looked back to see that the boats had turned right away from me heading towards what I found out to be the first lock. I walked back along the towpath to where the boats were tied up. Mr Watson was already on the edge of the lock releasing the water from the chamber.

I confronted Sarah-Anne again. 'Now what do you want me to do?'

'Stay there. You can pull the butty from one lock to the next and don't let it bang around in the lock.'

'What's a lock?'

'My God, don't you know anything?'

'Evidently not. I think somebody needs to tell me.'

Sarah-Anne was not well pleased with a kid that had just left school. She had been born on the canal and had grown up with more or less nothing else in her life. She knew everything that needed to be known about working boats going about their daily business on the canal. Despite my knowledge of Latin and the classics, I had little or no practical knowledge about anything. Maybe that was what my father wanted from me. At that moment in time I realised that I knew precious little about anything practical.

She jumped off the butty taking a cabin shaft with her. It was a small boat hook that was always left on the cabin top. You could always pull on a rope but you could never use it to push the boat into the middle of the canal. You needed a short handled boat hook – a cabin shaft.

She took the rope off the butty mast and handed it to me. 'Hang on to that and don't let the boat float off.'

She then left me and went to open the lock gates while Mr Watson guided the *John Peel* into the lock. I had no idea what had happened to Mrs Watson as she was nowhere to be seen. I later found out that she was preparing the next lock. It was called lock wheeling or simply setting the road.

Sarah-Anne closed the bottom gates of the lock and then disappeared from view only to return to sit down on the balance beam keeping an eye on me. She wasn't of course she was watching her father take the motor out of the lock. Upon closing the top gate, Sarah-Anne quickly wound up the paddles releasing the water. It came out in such force that I had quite a job holding on to the boat to stop it being swept away. The water eased and Sarah-Anne opened the offside lock gate before stepping over to the other gate so that I could pull the boat into the lock.

That simple task was more difficult than I had imagined. Being a 70ft long narrow boat entering into a 7ft wide lock, the boat had to be straight and in line otherwise it just wouldn't go and there would be a substantial amount of banging around. Sarah came to my help and pushed the butty with the cabin shaft to avoid the boat hitting the entrance of the lock. I took the rope up the lock side and eased it into the lock. Once in the lock I then had to stop it. I didn't but Sarah-Anne did. She put a couple of turns of the rope around one of the bollards on the lock side and the boat slowed and stopped.

She left me with the rope as she went to close the bottom gates of the lock before releasing the water from the intermediate pound. She made everything look so easy. I guessed that it was more skill and practice that she used rather than brute strength. There was a lot for me to learn.

I took the slack up on the rope and kept the fore end up against the top gate until it was opened and the sluices closed.

'What do we do now?' I asked.

'Wait for the next lock to be emptied. Dad's doing that now.'

'How many locks are there?'

'On the cut hundreds but here there are just eight.'

'Eight! How many hours will that take?'

'Hours? Minutes. Only about half an hour and then we can get up to Anglesey for loading.'

Anglesey? That was an island of the coast of North Wales. It would take a fortnight to get there. I found out that it was not that Anglesey but a coal wharf near Brownhills. My geography needed to be re-aligned.

She turned and left me to bow haul the boat out of the lock and up along the short pound to the next lock where she was opening the gates. I tried to give the butty a straight pull out of the lock but it was caught by the outflow from the by-wash that pushed the bow across the face of the lock. Sarah-Anne was aware of this and stood at the tail of the lock leaning on the cabin shaft easing the butty into the correct position. When the bow was in the lock she moved to the stern and straightened the boat up. It was my job to pull the boat into the lock and then stop its progress by strapping the tow rope around a bollard. That had been my first lesson. It was nowhere near the last and for the next five years I did nothing but learn everything about canal boat life that there was to know but at that moment I had little or no idea about anything.

The second lock was a repeat of the first as was the third and fourth. At the pound before the fourth and fifth I had a surprise. A horse appeared on the towpath connected to a long line with a loaded boat already in the lock. I was unsure what to do. Sarah-Anne came to my rescue. The lock would be left ready for us to proceed. She raised the horses tow rope over the butty that had pulled into the bank.

'Morning, Sarah-Anne. I see that you have a novice crew.'

'Morning, Mr Harris, more useless than useful.'

The boatman laughed. 'That's what you get from help off the bank.'

'And don't I know it. I have no idea what dad was thinking.'

'Nor anybody else.'

He was distracted by the horse that had looked around and then set off of his own accord leaving me to bow haul the boat into the lock while Sarah-Anne pushed the butty into the centre of the canal.

Finally we were at the top lock where Mr Watson was waiting for us with the motor. He was talking to the lock keeper while sitting on the balance beam of the top lock. Once we were in the lock and the water level began to rise he went back to the motor and reversed back to the lock. Once the top gate was open I pulled the butty up to the stern of the motor. Mr Watson was busy securing very short ropes. They were called cross straps as the butty would be secured close to the motor stern. I coiled up the rope and put it on the fore end cabin of the butty and ran back to climb on the stern where Sarah-Anne had taken off the tiller strings that had stopped it being caught on the lock side. We were off and underway.

Mr Watson waved farewell to the lock keeper and with the engine on tick-over passed a boat yard on the right hand side belonging to Ernie Thomas and then there was a little bridge taking the towpath over a canal arm leading to the Birchills Power Station. The arm was full of coal boats waiting to be emptied. There was no time to dwell as we headed off to Birchills Junction.

I didn't know whether Sarah-Anne was talking to me. I ventured a question. 'Can you tell me where we are going?'

'Anglesey Basin. I told you once. Don't you listen? We're picking up a load of coal but that won't be until Monday as nobody works on Sundays.'

We soon came upon the canal junction. It was one of many that I would encounter over my years on the boat but making a sharp right hand manoeuvre was sudden and unexpected. Mr Watson straightened up the boats with his expert steering and we entered into very narrow section of canal. It was a gauging stop. Mr Watson stepped off the motor and brought both boats to a standstill by passing a rope around a stump on the side of the canal. Even this simple act had its own name as I found out as I had no idea what they were talking about. They called it strapping and the stump was a strapping post. It was as if I could speak the language but have no understanding what was being said.

The Toll keeper came out of his little hut.

'Morning, Stan.'

'Morning, Len. Where are you bound for this fine morning?'

'Anglesey. We will be loading coal on Monday morning and will no doubt see you on the way back.'

'Where to then?'

'Market Drayton and then up to Ellesmere Port to collect a load of timber.'

'Have a good trip and I'll see you Monday all being well.'

With that, Mr Watson unhitched the rope from the bollard, put the motor into drive and we pulled away. I had the opportunity of getting away from Sarah-Anne to go with Mr Watson on the motor leaving Mrs Watson and Sarah-Anne on the butty. I was pleased to be out of the firing line of Sarah-Anne's sharp tongue.

Within the first bridges length Mr Watson slowed down and blew his horn. It was his only means of attracting attention. The men on the dock stopped work and waved. Mr Watson acknowledged their attention. I realised that Len Watson was a respected boatman and member of that fraternity. I was hoping that he would be a good teacher.

Beyond Worsey's boat yard was Pratt's Mill where Coast and Country Boats were unloading wheat. Mr Turner slowed the boats as he passed the moored boats. Beyond the wharf he opened up the throttle to make up speed as we took the turn around The Forest and over the railway aqueduct. The butty was still pulled up short to the rear of the motor.

'Go below, lad. There's nothing for you to do for the next hour or so. Unpack your bag and put your things away. Mrs Watson will give us a bite to eat for lunch.'

I went below to unpack my bag putting things into the cupboard and generally looking around the cabin.

I found my bed. It was in a cupboard! There was a drop leaf that spanned the gangway and inside the cupboard was a mattress and pillow. I refastened the drop leaf and found the food cupboard where the drop leaf was cantilevered to form a kitchen cum dining room table. My cupboard was empty except for two mugs, a tea caddy, an opened bag of sugar and an opened tin of condensed milk.

Mr Watson leaned down into the cabin. 'Josh, put some coal on the stove and we'll have a cup of tea. If you don't know how to make it, now's your chance to learn.'

I had no idea where the coal was but in such a small space it was impossible to hide anything. Below the cabin door was a coal box that was used as a step down into the cabin. Ha! It was the coal box that also had a small shovel. I scooped up some coal and turned my attention to the stove. It already had a kettle singing away as boiling kettles do. I moved the kettle to one side and put the coal on the fire before returning the kettle to carry on simmering.

I had seen my mother often enough make a pot of tea but had never been allowed near anything that was hot. Now I had to remember what she did. It wasn't that difficult. I found the tea pot and put in two spoons of loose tea. I poured on the boiling water and tea was made. It had a rather strange taste with the condensed milk but fresh milk was a rare treat that wouldn't keep in the warmth of the cabin. The warmth came not only from the stove but also from the Bolinder engine. It was a mighty beast with a strange exhaust noise that seemed to say bumpa, bumpa while running slowly and then bom bom bom bom as it picked up speed. It also had an enormous large flywheel that was spinning round. I found out later that I had to use this fly wheel to kick start the engine into life. At that moment I didn't know how much I would come to love that engine. I used to clean it every day.

The Wyrley and Essington Canal is what is known as a contour canal. There are no locks or didn't appear to be any and it followed the contour of the land. It wasn't called the Curly Wyrley without cause or reason. We had been travelling for about an hour and we could still see the cooling towers of Birchills Power Station possibly less than half a mile away. It was something that I didn't notice on that first trip.

Mrs Watson had two plates of bread and cheese that were handed over at a convenient bridge hole. I hadn't realised until then that I was hungry. It was thick slice off a loaf of bread and a lump of cheese that made little or no difference to my appetite.

I was surprised and impressed that Mr Watson could steer the boat putting his backside on the tiller bar while eating his bread and cheese with the plate on the cabin slide and then washing it down with a swig of tea. All this while we were underway!

There had been several entrances to canal basins and wharves but coming across what I thought was a major junction was the Cannock Extension at Pelsall Common. At Yorks Bridge there were already boats tied up at the pub but we pressed on. I guessed that Mr Watson would have liked to have arrived at Anglesey coal shoots that evening. We didn't of course as there was no pub there and we tied up alongside the Jolly Collier. Again he nudged the butty into the towpath with the motor tied up alongside.

Mr Watson showed me how to put in a mooring stake which was a long iron bar nearly 3ft long with a pointed end. It was driven into the towpath with a 4lb lump hammer until there were only a few inches above ground. There were two stakes, one at each end of the boat. It was tying the mooring rope to these stakes that secured the boat to the bank. I was much impressed. From here on that was another one of my jobs.

Len took me to one side. 'Josh, it's Saturday night. After our evening meal that you will have by yourself in the motor cabin, it's bath night for us where we all have a strip wash, get changed and go to the pub. In future that will be your routine as well. The washing order is Sarah-Anne first, followed by Mrs Watson and then me. You will stay on the *John Peel* until everybody is washed, dried and dressed. Have you got that?'

'Yes, Mr Watson. What do I wash in?'

'You can use the hot water in the kettle and I've given you a dipper that's hanging up by the stove. You need that for all you washing. You will do your own and hang it up in the engine room to dry. Oh, that's another one of your jobs; you need to find a tap, wherever we stop and fill all the cans with water yours and ours. We don't have running water on the boat so go sparingly with it.'

'Yes, Mr Watson.'

'Go and wash your hands. In a few minutes Ma will be serving you chicken broth for dinner.'

I left him to go into the motor cabin. It seemed strangely still and quiet when the engine wasn't running. I found the dipper. It was a galvanised bowl with a handle. I learnt how to not only fill the bowl but open the cabin door and throw the waste water away. I also tied up a piece of string in the engine room to act as a washing line for when I did my washing. I heard a knock on the cabin side.

'Josh, I've your dinner here.'

It was Mrs Watson with a pudding basin. It was my chicken broth and a large slice of bread on top.

'Thank you, Mrs Watson.' I said as I took the basin from her.

Boat cabin stove, dipper and windlass

I went into the cabin pulling the doors round. This was my little world. I lowered the cupboard table and started on my meal.

It was a strange sort of meal. It was definitely chicken tasting but I never found any pieces of chicken. It was mainly potatoes and root vegetables and maybe lentils but I wasn't sure. I only had a knife to eat it with. I couldn't find a fork or a spoon other than the tea spoon I had previously used. If that was all that I had in the way of cutlery then that's all that I had. I speared the vegetables and mopped up the gravy with the bread. It was different and was my introduction to one pot cooking.

After the meal I washed the dish up in the dipper and put everything away. I would return the basin to Mrs Watson the following day. I looked through my things. I only had one change of clothes and I would have to go out to the pub in the clothes I was wearing. I sat and waited. It was a longer wait than I expected. I had almost given up. It was getting dark and I had unrolled the cross bed and sat on it facing the cabin doors until I heard the knock on the cabin site. It was the signal to get up and go.

Saturday night for the canal boating fraternity was a complete surprise to me. All week the boaties went from one end of the country to the other alone and just seeing each other in passing. In a way it's a very lonely sort of life. On Saturday nights with some money in their pocket they all went to the pub. It started with seeing who was there as it was never the same group of people. Not only would there be passing acquaintances but also relatives, uncles, aunts, cousins and even brothers and sisters each with their entourage. It was an entourage as no member of the immediate family was left on the boat. They were all there, two, three and even four generations. The evening might have started by asking and telling who was going where with what but that all gave way with drinking beer that ended up by singing and generally having a good time. There always seemed to be somebody that could knock a tune out on a piano and occasionally somebody would bring along a melodeon or squeeze box. I think that they had their own favourites that had never seen the hit parade.

On this first occasion for me I went along with the Watson family. Len had put on what looked like a well worn suit complete with waistcoat and a silver hunter pocket watch. Mrs Watson had abandoned her chintz apron and wore a cotton print dress and cardigan as there was every likelihood that there would be a chill in the night air. Sarah-Anne looked radiant. She had her hair brushed or had it brushed for her and it cascaded down over her shoulders. Her bright red cheeks seemed redder somehow and she too was wearing a cotton print dress but she still wore her boots. Maybe that was all the footwear that she possessed.

There were all sorts of pleasantries and banter between the families as we arrived and it was left to Mr Watson to go to the bar to get served. He had a pint of mild beer, his wife and daughter each had half a pint of beer. It didn't seem to matter that Sarah-Anne was still only 15. I had a surprise when he handed me glass of what I thought was beer.

'Here, lad. Here's half a shandy. I've got you 5 Woodbines and a box of matches. This is the first and last time that I'm buying you beer and fags. In future, you can buy your own.'

I took the packet of 5 cigarettes and put them in my jacket pocket together with the matches. My dad would have had a fit if he knew that Len Watson had bought me beer and cigarettes. Yes, I had a crafty smoke as school, everybody had and I had emptied a few glasses after a drinks party but never had anybody ever bought them for me.

We went to sit down at a table but Len was up on his feet talking to people that he singled out. Sarah-Anne gave her a mother a smile and then went to stand next to a young guy. I was left with Mrs Watson.

'That's our Sarah-Anne's fella. They've been keen on

each other from when they were just 7 or 8. I think that they are meant for each other.'

I began to wonder whether it was part of an arranged marriage but didn't have time to complete that thought process when Mrs Watson added more. 'One day Sarah-Anne tells me that they want their own pair of boats and that Eddie, that's his name, his ambition is to be a Number One'

'What's that, Mrs Watson?'

'A Number One, is master of his own boat and takes great pride in his and the boats appearance. You can always tell a Number One by the way his brasses shine and his ropes are scrubbed white. I think that's what Sarah-Anne would like as well.'

'And in the meantime she is stuck with me, a bloke that knows nothing.'

Mrs Watson turned to look at me.

'You're clever lad by all accounts and that you are a scollard. You can read and write and you know your numbers. None of us can. I never went to school nor Len. I'm not sure what our Sarah-Anne knows but you don't need any of that to be a Number One.'

Now that was a revelation. For all their knowledge about the canal and working the boats nobody could read or write. All my thoughts had moved away from arranged marriages to just taking in the simple fact of clever people being illiterate.

I offered to buy Mrs Watson another drink but she told me that Len wouldn't hear of anybody else buying his wife a drink and I was to get my own.

I had no interest in the pub. I finished my drink and left. Walking along the towpath all was quiet except for

Boatman's cabin

the noise coming from the pub. I lit a cigarette and tried to take stock of my life. I came to the conclusion that at that moment I didn't have one.

CHAPTER THREE

I tried to get settled in the cross bed on the *John Peel* only to be woken up when the pub emptied and the boats banged about as people came on board. I guessed they gave me no thought or consideration. The next time I was woken up was by a banging on the cabin side.

'Wakey, wakey. Here's your breakfast. You need to make your own tea.'

It was Len waking me up.

I clambered out of bed, found my trousers, pushed back the slide and put my head over the cabin roof. It was a beautiful morning. All was still and quiet with just the bird song to be heard. I found a bowl of porridge on the cabin roof. I still had no spoon. I would have to eat it with my knife. I retreated back into the cabin, dropped the table and sat on the side of the cross bed contemplating my situation. The porridge was nice and creamy and sweet. I guessed that it had been made with condensed milk.

I looked at the stove. The fire had gone out overnight. Damn. I should have made it up the previous night and banked it down. Now I had no hot or even luke warm water. I quickly dressed for the day that started by clearing out the ash from the stove. I needed paper and kindle and coal I knew that I had some in the coal box. Looking around the boat I now realised why there was never paper of any description near the 'bucket and chucket'. I would have to improvise. I found some oily rag and some wood already chopped to size in the coal bucket and that was sufficient to get the fire going. I was thankful for the box of matches that Len had bought me. I needed to make sure that I always had a box of dry matches should the fire ever go out. I went up in the hatch to go on deck. The drinking water was kept in cans that sat alongside the chimney. It was quite a difficult procedure lifting the can to fill the kettle. There was a knack to everything. I was on a steep learning curve of just learning to do the basics.

Len came on to the *John Peel* to see how I was faring.

'What happened to you last night?' he asked.

'Came back to sort out my bed and try to get some sleep.'

'Let me tell you about today. Nobody works on a Sunday. We are supposed to work 8 hours a day five days a week but that doesn't pay the bills. We need to get round to Anglesey by 8 tomorrow morning. It's not far and if we are underway by 6 we will make it in good time.'

'What are we doing today?' I asked.

'Martha, Mrs Watson, is doing the weekly wash. It's a fine drying day so she will do the sheets as well. You need to come around the boats with me making sure that everything is in good working order. You need to fill the cans later after Martha has finished doing the washing. It will only be bread and cheese for lunch and another bowl of broth for your dinner. Now clear up here and give me a hand at mopping down the boats.'

My day off was one of unpaid work. It started by mopping down the cabin roof and wiping the cabin sides before cleaning the fore deck. Len took me through the cabin to check the stern gland. From now on it would be down to me to make sure that I kept the leak to a minimum. We also had a look at the bilge. There was about six inches of water that had accumulated. I had no idea where that had come from. It had to be pumped out and that was another experience. What we had on the boat was something like a portable hand pump. It was just an iron pipe with a branch near the top. There was a rod and plunger in the pipe and by lowering it and then raising it had the effect of pumping the bilge water out and away over the boat side. The first two pulls were easy but after a few minutes my arms began to ache with the continuous effort. Len saw my difficulty and took over until we could draw no more water.

We then moved into the engine room to check on the fuel level, sump oil level and generally give the engine a wipe down with an oily rag. I had burnt the previous one and that would be the last time I did that.

So the day slowly progressed. We polished all the brasses on both boats and took a scrubbing brush to the white rope fenders fore and aft. Len told me that the fenders on the rear of *John Peel* were known as Tip-cats. It was something else to be put away in my memory bank for when needed. I used all the water from my cans scrubbing the fenders and was sent along the towpath to find the tap.

I made tea. I was handed a piece of bread and lump of cheese for lunch and cleaned and polished everything that was visible until dinner arrived and I went back to my cabin to take my evening meal. I couldn't believe that my father realised what he was sending me to. I could always jump ship and walk back. Walsall was still only three miles down the road and we had been out boating all day! This really was slow progress.

I lit the oil lamp in the cabin that provided the only source of illumination and took out a book that I had permanently borrowed from the school library. I didn't think that they would miss just one book. It was an adventure book by Walter Scott whoever he was and the book was *Ivanhoe*. I was surprised when Robin Hood appeared im its pages. It was a poor light to read by but I managed somehow and my eyes became heavy until I couldn't keep them open any longer. I made up the fire and banked it down, turned off the oil lamp and rolled into bed. I didn't remember anything further until there was banging on the cabin side. It was like a clap of thunder. It was my early morning call.

'Breakfast's on the cabin top. We need to be away within the hour.'

Len had delivered his message. There was no turning over in the warmth of the blankets. I put on the clothes that I had taken off the night before, found my breakfast and tried again to eat porridge with just a knife.

I raked the fire, put some more coal on and put the full kettle on to boil. At least I could have a warm drink and wash in warm water in what was rather a chilly morning. Putting my nose out of the door I realised how much I needed that warm coat. Len was already in the engine room starting the blow lamp on the Bolinder cylinder head. It was Monday and a working day and there was no time to be lost.

I helped to slip the lines off the butty while Sarah-Anne untied the mooring ropes and pulled up the stakes making it look easy. She jumped on board and we were underway. It was almost 6 o'clock. I couldn't remember ever being up at that time before but from here on it would be each and every day. On Sundays we could have a lie in until 7!

Already we were being passed in the opposite direction

by horse boats already loaded. They had been waiting since Saturday lunch time to get moving and they weren't hanging around. Len gave them all a nod as they passed on the inside. At Catshill Junction we carried straight on with the Daw End Branch going off to our right. Then almost without warning we veered to the left at the turnover bridge at the top of Ogley Locks. There were 30 evidently but not for us today. There was an all brick aqueduct over the A5, Watling Street, before the wide expanse of Anglesey Basin lay before us.

Len brought the *Rosemary* and turned both boats together bringing them alongside the coal loading shoot. We had a few minutes to wait that irritated Len making him unapproachable. He gave me a shovel. I didn't ask what it was for. I didn't want to vent his anger and frustration out on me when I hadn't done anything.

The coal was being tipped from coal rail wagons and it was an uneven load. That's why I had the shovel. When the boat had a 20 ton load it was moved along so that a further 20 tons could be tipped into the butty. It was my job to move the coal around so that it was more or less even and the boat sat upright. A leaning boat would never get through the locks.

Once loaded, Len was keen to be away. I was put in the butty to sort out the load while moving. We weren't going to waste precious time being tied up while the boat was being trimmed. I was surprised that it was Mrs Watson steering the butty and Sarah-Anne shovelling with me. She was as strong as me and it didn't take long for us to finish getting the boat running level. We made our way to the cabin where she disappeared into the cabin to emerge with mugs of tea. Her father could get his own while we

Ogley Junction

Anglesey Basin at the end of the Coal Trade

were underway.

Taking a pair of loaded narrowboats around the Wyrley on a 90 ft line was quite an experience. Turning the corner at Catshill we could see Birchills Power Station emitting smoke and clouds of water vapour and then it was gone only to return again as we passed it at Birchills Junction on our left two hours later. It was to appear again behind us as we entered Short Heath.

The various toll stops enabled Mrs Watson to dish up food. It was mainly chunks rather than slices of bread with cheese and pickle onions or cauliflower or red cabbage to add some sort of flavour to the blandness of the everyday food. We had tea more or less each and every hour. It really was a long journey from Anglesey to Wolverhampton past Sneyd, Rough Wood, Holly Bank Basin and the Bentley Canal at Wednesfield Junction before we were brought to a standstill at Horsley Fields in what I thought was Wolverhampton. It was close but the Main Line was ahead of us and we made a swift turn between boats travelling in what looked like all direction, left, right and wanting our place in the stop. It wasn't long before we were travelling through what looked like canyons of factory walls and then coal wharves serving the town. At last we drew up before Broad Street Bridge. We would have to wait our turn the following morning. The locks had been closed for the night. It had taken us all day to travel about 20 miles from Anglesey to Wolverhampton Top Lock. It would be an early start on Tuesday and a long hard day. I couldn't believe that after a day of not seeing a single lock we had 21 all in one go. I resolved myself to having a long and hard day. It was an early night for me in the motor cabin.

We had tied up nowhere near the top lock as there were

several boats in front of us and before long the queue of boats stretched out behind us. Everything seemed calm but there was an undercurrent of feeling of impatience. All the boatmen wanted to clear the locks and be on their way as soon as possible. 7.30 the following morning couldn't come fast enough.

I had my early morning call at 5 a.m. which was not the norm. Once out on a lock free road it would be 4.10 so on that particular morning little did I know it but I had been given a lie in!

Len started the blow lamp on the Bolinder cylinder head at 6.30 and had the engine running by 7. He didn't want to be pushed to the back of the waiting boats because his engine wouldn't start. We weren't the first nor the last and there was a cacophony engines as all the boats started their engines waiting for the lock keeper to unchain the top gates. At precisely 7.30 the lock keeper arrived unfastened the chains and set the lock. It would be an hour or so before any boat from the bottom lock would emerge from under Littles Lane Bridge.

We edged our way forward and it was almost 8 as Len put *John Peel* in the lock. Today the working order had changed. Sarah-Anne was setting the lock. Martha was steering the *John Peel* while Len was with me bow hauling the *Rosemary* in the locks.

When I asked how many locks were there, I was shocked when they said 21. I thought that the Walsall 8 had about 7 too many but 21 – it would take all day. This was not so. We had to get a move on as the following boat crew were good humouredly pushing us out of each and every lock. They only raised a paddle when the bottom gates were opened and *Rosemary* exited the lock on a 6 inch tidal

Horsley Fields Junction

wave with the gates being slammed shut behind us. In one way it meant rapid progress for us and less pulling so that we managed to keep up. It was becoming a slick operation. Everybody knew what they were doing and the rack and pinion paddles were being rattled up with what seemed consummate ease. I found out later that like all things there was a knack to doing it quickly and easily and more importantly when. That was for me to learn during my time on the boats.

The locks came at regular intervals and if the number hadn't been carved on the balance beams I would never have been able to keep track. Below lock 16 the pound between locks became longer and Martha waited for us so that she could tow the boat rather than me and Len pulling it on a long line.

Once below the Stafford Road Bridge gone were the factory walls that were replaced by trees. Along one pound the canal ran alongside the racecourse before reaching the bottom lock, number 21. We were at last off the Brumycham cut and on to the leafy Staffordshire and Worcestershire Canal. Len was back on *John Peel* with Sarah-Anne and I sat on the cabin roof of the butty while Martha took the helm.

We weren't travelling along the Staffs and Worcs very far when Sarah-Anne leapt off and ran along the towpath. I wondered where she was going. I soon found out because under a rather elegant grey painted bridge there was a lock that announced the start of the Shropshire Union Canal. Sarah-Anne was just opening the top gate as Len put the nose of *John Peel* under what was the turnover bridge taking the Staffs and Worcs towpath over the Shroppie as it went off in the direction of Stafford. The finger post didn't say Stafford but Great Haywood. I had no idea where that was. All the canal junctions and bridges all had their own names. Despite not being able to read them, the boating fraternity knew each and every one by name. I had no idea how anybody could remember so many names and what's more they recognised each and every one as they were all individually different.

The lock at Autherley Junction, for that's where we were, was a joke. The difference in levels was only 6 inches. I was later told that for every lock of water coming down the Wolverhampton flight, the Shropshire Union was allowed one lock of water albeit only 6 inches difference in levels. I never found out who counted the number of times the locks were used.

By the time I had helped to pull *Rosemary* into the lock Len was talking to the lock keeper who also registered what boat was carrying what cargo as they entered this particular waterway. He was also the toll man who measured the freeboard and made a note on the boat

'Cut End' Autherley Junction

ticket. We were soon on our way and again the crew order
had changed; I was on the *Rosemary* with Sarah-Anne
while Len and Martha were on the *John Peel*. It didn't take
me long to realise that Sarah-Anne was under instructions
to show me how to steer the butty. It didn't go well.

Going north from Autherley Junction or Cut End as
the boating fraternity call it, the canal is more or less as
straight as a dye. Just what was needed for me to first
steer in a straight line and then work out how to tackle
bends and bridges. Could I keep the boat progressing
in a straight line? I could not. It seemed to have a mind
of its own first this way and then that. When I tried to
straighten up it only became worse. I had the ire of Sarah-
Anne as she was always pulling or pushing the tiller arm
the opposite way that I had decided upon. I did eventually
work it out but not on that first trip.

At one narrow section it appeared that we were high
above a road. I was told that it was Stretton Aqueduct
over the A5. Over the A5? Wasn't that the road we passed

over two days ago? We were only about 20 miles further on and we had been boating for two days! This really was hard slow progress.

The first lock before our destination at Market Drayton was at a place called Wheaton Aston. It seemed like a bottle neck with boats waiting to traverse in both directions. We took our turn. It was one of the few occasions when the boat crews could swap stories: fallen tree in the Rocket: one of the paddles at Audlem was broken and drained a pound overnight: 'Diddler' Danny Walker was a dad again; another girl when he was desperate for a son. I heard the gossip which at that time meant nothing to me.

Once through the lock we were back making what I considered good time as there were no hold ups. The times when Sarah-Anne grabbed the tiller were becoming fewer and her temper began to subside that is until the next impending disaster. She was convinced that nobody off the bank would ever be able to steer or work a narrow boat. I guess she had her reasons for coming to this conclusion. At that precise moment my only concern was to make sure that I didn't steer the boat up the bank or get between another pair of working boats travelling in the opposite direction.

Sarah-Anne seemed to know or be known by everybody that passed with a 'Good day, Missy'; 'Hello Sarah-Anne where you off to?' She had an answer for everybody while her father looked back to make sure that we didn't get tangled up with the other boats. It was a nice day and being out in the country Sarah-Anne's ire washed over me.

My idyll was sharply interrupted when we arrived at yet another canal junction that teemed with activity from the pub to the boat yard and stables. We didn't stop but slowed before pressing on. Norbury was an important canal junction but that was all. There wasn't even a village just the pub and a couple of houses. Beyond the junction there was a wood. Martha explained to me that there was a screaming ghost in Betton Wood and no boatman would ever moor there overnight.

We were soon out of Betton Wood and plunged into the Rocket. The canal was narrow, barely enough room for boats to pass with steep high embankments with overhanging trees the sunlight making a mottled effect on the canopy. It was an eerie place. And then we were high up in the fields only to be confronted by Tyrley locks, just five this time. They seemed to have been cut straight out of the red sandstone rock. Never mind the scenery, get the boats through and Market Drayton was just a mile and half away but not before we passed through my first tunnel of many. I had no idea that canals went underground as well as over roads and railways and rivers probably. I really was on a journey of discovery.

It was early evening when we tied up at the coal wharf in Market Drayton. It had given Martha time to cook something for the evening meal and we had a relaxed evening. I helped Len sort out the motor alongside the wharf. That would be unloaded first followed by the butty. We would take on the shovelling into tubs or wheelbarrows for the wharf men to take it away from the water's edge. They would start work at 8 o'clock and with a bit of luck they might open up at 7.30.

It was at times like those that I needed something to do. I didn't have enough cigarettes to chain smoke all evening and going to the pub was not strictly legal. What I needed was another book; a good book preferably but even an old newspaper that could fulfil at least two other possibilities would be welcome.

Len was up at his usual time which meant I was as well. We mopped down the cabin roof and sides before polishing the brass decoration on the chimney and engine exhaust. He was a very proud man and this was reflected in the appearance of him and his boats.

At 7.30 the coal yard gates opened and we could start unloading the coal. It was really difficult getting a shovel into the loose lying lumps of coal. Len explained that we needed a lade hole that was to get down to the bottom of the boat so that we should shovel the coal up more easily. He was right it did become easier but there were still 20 tons to move. When that was completed, the butty was moved up to the wharf and the process repeated. Shovelling 40 tons of coal before breakfast is a tiring job. We had a short break before going back into the hold of the boats again and sweeping up every last piece of slack and coal dust so the boats were impeccably clean. Len then showed me how to put up the canvas sheeting on both boats. It didn't matter about any rain falling on coal but it did on virtually every other cargo we were likely to carry.

While this was being sorted out Martha took Sarah-Anne into the market town to buy everyday items. I asked for some razor blades which were top of my shopping list and there was no chance of me buying any while working on the boats.

It was lunch time before we set off again and we were soon on the 5 locks at Addingham and then the 15 at Audlem. They were slow and harder than the well worked locks on the Wolverhampton 21. Finally we eased passed the two locks at Hack Green. That was the last of the narrow locks. We pressed on to Nantwich on the old

Chester Canal with its double locks so we could take the boats through together.

We tied up at Barbridge Junction ready for yet another early start on Thursday. We made what I considered to be excellent progress. I had yet another shock at Chester as the canal followed the City Walls until it suddenly dropped off with a three chamber staircase at North Gate Locks. We had to wait for a pair of boats coming up and we couldn't pass in the locks. It felt as if the bottom had fallen out of the canal as the boats descended. I was pleased when the cross straps were attached to the motor to make the last 10 miles to Ellesmere Port. We had to lock down into the basins where there was a junction with the partly tidal Manchester Ship Canal with the mighty River Mersey just beyond. The timber had already been unloaded was waiting for us and a few others to collect it to be taken further on its journey.

We tied up for the night again waiting for the day porters to load the timber. I quizzed Len where we were taking it.

'Back to your neck of the woods – the Black Country.'

We would retrace our outward journey with the Audlem 15 and Wolverhampton 21 to contemplate. It occurred to me that even with the waiting round to unload and now loading there was never an easy day.

We made Cow Lane Bridge that night and Audlem the following night. It was Saturday which meant an early finish and a visit to the pub. Before that I went into the town and found an old bookshop and asked the old guy who ran the shop for a couple of adventure novels. He found a copy of C.S.Forrester's Midshipman Hornblower. That simple event changed my five years on the boats.

Before that there were the long straight stretches of the

New Main Line
Rattle Chains Brick Works

Shroppie where I continued my steering instruction. I was getting the hang of steering and keeping a straight line. Also fully laden going up the locks was different. When the lock I was in with the butty had the top gate open Len released the water from the next lock. I was given a long boat hook, 15ft to 16ft in length with a wooden button that would fit onto my shoulder. I could push the boat out rather than try to pull it out on a rope. It worked really well. It was a straight push for the length of the lock and when clear of the top gate there was nothing to stop it from finding its own way to the next lock. As if by magic by the time it reached the entrance of the lock the gates opened and found its own way in. The boat hook was needed to stop it banging into the cill below the upper gate. We made good and steady progress.

All this bow hauling on the shorter flights of locks at Addingham and Tyrley stood me in good stead for

Audlem and Wolverhampton flights. On the summit level
of the Birmingham Main Line the canal was busy with
local traffic. It was mainly coal coming from the Cannock
coal field to the electricity generating power station in
Wolverhampton affectionately called the 'Ampton Light'.
Beyond that the skyline was dominated by the blast
furnaces at Bilston and then we entered the Coseley
Tunnel with its two tow paths. We went through at our
full speed of 3 miles an hour.

After Tipton Factory Bridge we came to the three locks.
The Old Main Line veered off to the right. Along the offside
was the weighing house where the boats were weighed and
on the towpath side was the Boatman's Church. We had to
wait our turn as the locks were in seemingly constant use.
We eased our passage through the locks and within a short
distance the New Main Line stretched out before us in a
straight line for as far as the eye could see with the railway
keeping us company. The LMS express locomotives roared
past in both directions with the engine driver giving us a
blast on his whistle. I had the feeling that we were all part
of the transport family.

This all changed beyond a railway bridge when Len
slowed down and shortened the towing rope as he made
a very sharp left hand turn. I later found out that this was
the strangely named Pudding Green Junction and was a
short section of canal to the top of Riders Green Locks
and the commencement of the Walsall Canal. I never
found out what the name of this bit of canal was called
but at the top of the locks it went off to the right serving
more factories in the environs of West Bromwich.

The Riders Green Locks were seemingly fitted in between
factory walls with the occasional wharf. To say that they were

well used was an understatement we were passed by two horse drawn day boats on the way up as we locked down. At the tail of the last lock there was a large Great Western Railway interchange basin on the right and the Haines Branch on the left. On a very short towing rope, Len made the turn into the branch canal where after about half a mile we tied up at Tailby and Cox's timber yard.

It had been a long and hard day of double locking having traversed 32 locks from Cut End where we moored overnight. We had to wait until the following morning to be unloaded.

It was Saturday and I wondered what Len had in mind. The Haines Branch was not the best spot for tying up for a night in the pub.

'Where do you intent going this weekend?' I asked him after our evening meal.

'I'm not staying here. I need to pick up orders for next week from the Public Wharf. We are on the Walsall Canal so it will be an easy run around with no locks. There will pubs enough when we get there.'

'Could I take the bike and go to see mom and dad?'

'I don't see why not. You will need to be back on Sunday night for a 6 o'clock start on Monday morning.'

'Can I go now?'

'Sure, why not? See you on Sunday on the Public Wharf.'

I didn't need to be told twice and I took the old bike off the cabin roof and rode along the towpath into Walsall where I left the canal to take the main road back home. I had a welcome that I was unprepared for.

Mother was at home and immediately dispatched me to the bath room. She took all my clothes and put them to the wash. Evidently I stank and my clothes were

Coseley Tunnel

a total disgrace. I enjoyed the warmth of the bath and found some of my wardrobe so that I was presentable at lunchtime when father returned from the factory. He was not altogether pleased to see me.

'What the Hell are you doing here? I paid that bloke to look after you and keep you on his boat.'

'He has and he did. He's tied up at the Public Wharf and it's nice to see you again.'

'I need to tell him not to let you come back here especially at weekends.'

'Dad, leave the boy alone. I'm pleased to see him and get him clean again. I think that he also needs a good meal inside him. I can't imagine what he's been given to eat.' It was mother coming to my assistance in dealing with my father.

'Hmm. He looks well enough. I guess the fresh air's doing him good whatever he's been given to eat.' was my father's assessment of my condition.

It made for an uneasy afternoon and I was pleased when he went out to the 'club' to drink with his cronies leaving me at home with mother. She put the radio on as there was a concert she wanted to tune in to. I went to my bedroom where I collapsed and had the best night's sleep I'd had for two weeks.

I tried to keep out of my father's way on Sunday morning and after the midday dinner, I collected my things as well as a bag of old newspapers, said goodbye to my mother and rode to the Public Wharf. Len had finished cleaning the boats and was preparing for another week not knowing where he was bound.

CHAPTER FOUR

At that point of my story I was distracted. We had turned the corner so that the locks were now in front of us. Ernie Thomas still had his yard on the opposite bank with two tugs tied up. I recognised them as being two of the Joshers that he had salvaged from the war time bombing raid that had hit their Birmingham Depot at Farmer's Bridge. Ernie had never been one to miss an opportunity.

The towpath rose up in a small bridge over what was the entrance to the Birchills Power Station arm. It was now stanked off and filled in. There would be no more coal boats unloading there.

'Dad, dad, how did reading a book change things?'

It was Oliver pulling on my sleeve. He didn't want half a story. I looked down at my son. He was looking up at me. The Ernie Thomas boats or the disused canal basin had no interest to the lad.

'OK, here's how it changed things for me.'

Each evening after the evening meal I would light the paraffin oil lamp and read a chapter of my book. Sometimes the meal would be a bit late due to events of the day and it was one of those occasions that Len actually found me reading Ivanhoe. He was overcome with curiosity.

'What are you doing?'

'Oh, just reading a book.'

'What does it tell you?'

'It doesn't tell me anything. It's a story about a knight in

Walsall Top Lock

the reign of Richard the Lionheart.'

'A story?'

'Yes, most books are stories. Some are full of information like arithmetic or maps and things like that but this is a story of a knight called Ivanhoe. It was written about 100 years ago by a Scottish writer, Walter Scott.'

'Never heard of him. Is it a good story?'

'It's alright. I brought it with me from home and I bought another about the navy in Nelson's time. It was the best I could find in Audlem. When we are next in Walsall, I need to go home and collect a couple more.'

He left me to have my meal while it was still warm.

It was a few days later. We had just unloaded and had made our way to the next wharf for collecting some carboys to take to Oldbury when Len came to see me in the cabin.

'Josh, I don't know how to ask but this is my oldest family possession.' He said handing me a large black Moroccan bound book.

I took the book. It was a bible. I opened the front cover

to realise that it was a family bible with a list of names. The last entry was Sarah-Anne 20th June 1920.

'It's your family bible.' I said as I handed it back to him.

'Er, I don't know how to ask but could you read it?'

'I think what you are asking is could I read it to you and Martha?'

'I don't think that anybody has ever read any part of it. Would you? You wouldn't mind?'

'Len, I would be privileged to read parts to you. I don't know anybody that's read it from cover to cover. It's not a book like that. All the stories are there Adam and Eve, Moses and the Ten Commandments, Samson and Delilah, David and Goliath, Noah and the Ark leading up to John the Baptist and the coming of Jesus. All the stories are in there. Maybe I could read parts to you after our evening meal on Sunday. How does that sound?'

Len was overcome with emotion. He shook my hand. 'Thank you.' was all that he could say. He blew his nose on his well used handkerchief and left me with my supper cum dinner.

That was the start. Each and every Sunday evening after my evening meal, I would go and sit in the back cabin of the *Rosemary* and by the light of the paraffin lamp I read a short extract from the Old Testament. I think Len thought that I would read all of it but I moved from Adam and Eve to Moses and so on. All three Len, Martha and Sarah-Anne hung on my every word. It was a sort of bonding and I think at that moment I was part of their family. The fact that I was not of canal boating stock was forgotten; I was accepted.

It didn't end there. I remember the boat was tied up outside the Beehive at Tipton on the Old Main line one weekend. Everybody was in the pub. I had bought a glass of beer and was sitting on the wall bordering on the canal when a young girl approached me. I had seen her on her family boats but that's all.

'You are Josh, aren't you?'

'Yeah, I'm Josh. You need to remind me of your name.'

'It's Maisy. Mom and Dad wanted to ask you something but are – I don't know the word – but didn't want to impose on you and were afraid to ask.'

'Maisy, I can't think what they are worried about. I'm the one who knows little or nothing about the cut and they seem to know everything.'

'It's not about that. We've had a letter and none of us can read it.'

'Ah, I see. Would you like me to read the letter to them?'

'Would you mind? Please say that you will.'

'Maisy, of course I'll read the letter. I have some writing paper and envelopes and stamps that I use to write home to my parents and if you want a reply I will write it for you.'

'Can we do it now? I'll go in the pub and they can come to see you here.'

'Now is as good a time as any.'

Maisy ran back to the pub. I guess that she was possible a bit older than Sarah-Anne but I never was any good at judging young girls ages.

A few minutes later Maisy came with her mother and father together with the letter that was un-opened.

I realised that in a society that weren't driven by the written word letters were either good or bad news. Getting any sort of letter delivered to boats on the canal was a traumatic experience. These people were no exception.

I was handed the letter and tentatively opened it. I quickly scanned the letter and looked up smiling. It was good news.

'Mr and Mrs Weaver, this is a letter from Horace. Their daughter Clarice has just had a baby boy. They are planning to have the boy Christened, Albert George at the church in Newbold on Easter Sunday at 11 o'clock. They would like all the family to be there.'

The faces of the Weaver Family broke into smiles.

'Can you get there?' I asked.

'We will unless the Good Lord or the lock keeper at Curdworth stops us. There's no carrying on Good Friday or the Saturday that gives us two days to make the trip no matter where we finish up on the Brumycham Cut.'

'Do you want me to write back to them? They have put an address on the letter. It's care of the Greyhound Inn.'

'That's at Sutton Stop. That will find them.'

'The address is Hawkesbury Junction, Coventry.' I said rather perplexed wondering about where the letter was heading.

'That's the canal name. To us it's always been the Sutton Stop. Can you tell them that we will be there?'

'I'll go back and write it now and put it in the letter box in Owen Street.'

'Can I come with you?' Maisy asked.

'I can't see why not and you can put the letter in the box for me.'

Mr Weaver came and shook my hand as did Mrs Weaver. They were off back to the pub to announce the new addition to the family while I went back to the *John Peel* to write the letter.

It didn't take long and Maisy was attentive as I wrote the letter and addressed the envelope. It was finished by me adding the stamp of King George V. We walked from the boat along the road to Owen Street where I let Maisy put the letter in the letter box. This simple act was a watershed in her life. For me, it was just something run of the mill.

Walking back to the Beehive she took my hand in hers.

'Josh, do you have a girlfriend.'

'No.'

'Everybody thinks that you and Sarah-Anne are engaged.'

'That's not true. I'm not sure that she even likes me. It's more like tolerates me. I don't particularly like her.'

'Josh, can I be your girlfriend?'

'I can't see why not. What do I have to do to be your boyfriend?'

'You can start by holding my hand.'

'I think that I've already passed that test.'

'And you can kiss me.'

'I've never kissed a girl.'

'Then I'll be the first.' She said as she pushed me against a wall and pressed her lips on mine.

It wasn't the sort of first kiss that I had fantasised over but was all of a rush and over before I realised what was happening. This was all very sudden and totally unexpected. Maisy was a nice girl and I wondered what I was letting myself in for. I hoped for a good time.

We continued walking back to the Beehive where she went to tell her parents that she had posted the letter while I bought us both a glass of beer. Mr and Mrs Weaver were well pleased and I entered their circle of friends celebrating a new addition to their family.

When the towel was put on the pumps that were used for pulling the beer, which was a well recognised signal that the bar was closed, Maisy took me outside to the back of the pub where we had a second round of goodnight kissing.

This was altogether better as I held her closely to me.

Again it was over all too soon but I arranged to meet up with her again after lunch the following day. We strolled hand in hand along the towpath. It wasn't the most romantic of locations but we were only interested in each other. It was just catching up on life styles. Maisy had been born and brought on the canal as had her parents and their parents. She was really interested in where my parents lived and what school was like and was it hard learning to read and write. I could tell her all about school and living 'on the bank' but I couldn't remember learning to read or write. It was completely wiped from my memory. It was something that I could do and not even think about it. We sat on the balance beam of the top lock at Tipton Factory.

There were no boats passing so we weren't disturbed as we sat holding hands. We had no idea when we would ever meet up again and there was no obvious method of keeping in touch with each other. Her family were from the Coventry area and they mainly ran between Coventry and Birmingham where we were nearly always Shroppie bound.

Early evening we parted with a brief kiss. She went back to her parent's boat and I went back to the *John Peel*. My afternoon with Maisy hadn't gone unnoticed. That simple interlude caused a tsunami that I didn't see coming.

Len just thumped the cabin side announcing my meal was on the cabin roof. As usual I had it in the back cabin of the motor. Afterwards I washed my dish and put it ready for the next meal. It was time to read from the bible.

I politely knocked the butty cabin side before opening the doors and stepping down into the cabin. It was Len that led a verbal assault.

'What were you doing with that Weaver girl?' he demanded.

Boatman's Church, Tipton Factory Locks

'Minding my own business.' I retorted. It had nothing to do with him who I spoke to. If it had been my father it probably would have been a different matter but he wasn't.

'Don't talk to me in that tone. They aren't a well liked family. They aren't from around these parts.'

'If you must know, I read a letter they had received and wrote a reply for them. It was Maisy that posted it; beginning and end of story.'

'What were you reading their letters for?'

'They are like you, they can't read or write.'

'I forbid you to see her or read their letters again.'

'You can forbid all you like. I came here to read the bible in a Christian and charitable way. You've had the last reading from me and come tomorrow I will be going back to Walsall and you can stick your canal.'

I turned and left them.

Back in the cabin I was unsure whether I should leave straight away or the following morning. The way I felt it would be now. I started getting my things together. There was a knock on the cabin side.

'Go away!' I shouted.

It was Martha. 'Josh, can I see you for a minute?'

'What for to tell me who I can and can't see?'

'I'm sorry about Len. He regards you as family and wants to look after you. He was only trying to tell you about the Weaver family. Not everybody on the cut is good and sometimes we aren't sure. He, well none of us, wanted to upset you and I think that we have.'

'That's for sure. Some Christian family you turned out to be. Love they neighbour routine is just the words and that's the last thing you do.'

'Josh, that's not helpful. I came here to say sorry that we upset you and wanted you to come to read to us.'

'Martha, learn to read. I've done all the reading for you and Len.'

'Sarah-Anne was going to ask you to teach her to read and write.'

'Ha, she has a barbed tongue. She has not said one nice thing to me or about me. I pity the bloke that she ends up with. She should have gone to school. I'm not teaching her anything not because I can't but because she thinks knows everything already.'

'Josh, this is not good but I can see that you haven't appreciated what you have done for us.'

'That's about right. Everything for you and nothing for anybody else; a very Christian sentiment. I've had enough of, well not you personally, but Len and Sarah-Anne. You can get another slave. I was going now and after talking to you I definitely am leaving and going back home.'

'Your father will only bring you back here.'

'Maybe, maybe not. Over the past few weeks I've had a lesson in growing up. I won't be that school kid that he can order about. In future, he will have to ask.'

'Josh, I'm sorry if you think we've treated you badly we never meant to. We had no idea what you were like and were very wary of everything that you said and did. You have turned out to be the son that Len always wanted.'

'He should have tried the natural way.'

'He did but nothing ever came of it. Now I'm going to ask you to stay and sleep on it. Don't make a choice in anger. It never works out. You could end up falling out not only with us but your own folks and that's the last thing I want. Think about staying a bit longer.'

I gave in. 'I'll stay the night and as you say I'll sleep on it. As a matter fact I have no idea whether or not I will ever see the Weavers again. They are all going off to a Christening at Newbold wherever that is.'

'There, it's all a storm in a teacup. Newbold is a three day trip from here. It's their part of the country. I can't remember ever going there. Please stay, Josh. It means so much for me trying to keep my little family together.'

Martha really was more like the mother I wanted rather than the austere woman I had. I guessed that I would stay.

The following day it was business as usual and nothing more was ever said about the incident but it was the end of me reading the bible. I stayed with the Watson's and over the course of the next four years I learnt the trade of a working boatman. I never went back to see my parents in particular my father.

Oliver and I were just passing the locks when a horse drawn Joey came down the locks with a load of coal. It was one of Caggy's boats but Caggy was conspicuous by his

Gas Street Basin

absence it was just Ernie and Arthur and the horse of course.

While Oliver was distracted it gave me time to reflect on the lovely Maisy. I guessed that she had a boy friend in London and possibly one in Coventry and I was just a lad from the Black Country. However that didn't detract from the passion we had for each other. The next time we met up was in Gas Street, Birmingham. I took her to the pictures on Saturday night. There was a good film on at the West End but we never got around to watching it. On the following Sunday afternoon we spent the afternoon in the War Memorial Gardens that used to be Baskerville Basin. We vowed to meet up again and we did. On this occasion we didn't go to the cinema on Saturday night but back to her cabin while her parents were in the pub. That was altogether different yet the most enlightening and enjoyable experience that I had during my short adult life. I never saw Maisy again and had no idea what happened to her.

My musing stopped as the boat moved to the next lock and Oliver turned to me. I intended to return to my story before I was distracted with memories of Maisy but Oliver was pulling on my hand.

'Dad do horses ever fall in the canal?'

I had been holding on to Oliver so that he didn't fall in and he was now concerned about the horse.

'Not very often but when it does it really is a bad situation.'

'Have you ever seen a horse fall in the canal?'

'Not fall but what happened afterwards while he was in the canal.'

'What happened?'

It was yet another incident that I recalled.

We were somewhere in Tipton as I recall. We had dropped some chemicals off in Oldbury and were making good time back to Wolverhampton on the Old Main Line. We came to a sudden halt at the narrow next to the toll office near Rounds Wharf. There were boats every where and a fire engine parked on Canal Side. Our boats just bumped into all the others and at the toll stop Len and I got off.

The toll keeper came out to gauge the boats.

'Morning Arthur, what's going on?' Len asked.

'Morning, Len. 'Oss in the cut. Only a young 'un. Something must have startled him and he ended up in the pound. He's just below the Tip'n Green Top Lock.'

'We'll go and have a look to see if we can help. My mate will sort out the ticket.'

With that Len and I walked the short distance to the locks.

I had never seen Len get angry before. He had always

been in control of each and every situation. He was calm efficiency exemplified. When he looked down the pound to see what was going on he was livid. I had never heard a boatman swear before but he had a choice vocabulary to draw on.

What I could make out was a mass of people congregating around a large black object in the canal. Somebody had let all the water out between the first and second lock. What was left was black mud. The large object was the horse that was covered in slimy black mud. They had just put the horse down to stop him having more distress. Now they were just getting him out. It was not a pretty sight. We turned and walked back to the boats. I needed to know why Len had been so angry.

'Len, why couldn't they get the horse out?' I asked hoping that I wouldn't vent his anger towards me.

'Somebody let all the water out expecting the horse to walk out. With all that mud around nobody could walk out.'

'What should they have done?'

'Over the years that wasn't the first horse to fall in the canal. There are some places they even have steps so the horse can walk out. What they needed to do and nobody seemed to have any idea was to fill the pound to overflowing. The owner of the horse should have jumped in with the horse and led him to a spot where the horse could jump out.'

'What if there wasn't? I couldn't see where he could.'

'Then you have a second plan.'

'Which is?' This interrogation was like getting blood out of a stone.

'What you do is find some sturdy planks and have one end on the bank and the other in the canal as close to the horse as you can get them. You then wrap the horse in sacking. Anything would do to stop the ropes cutting in to him. The ropes, normally two would be enough; you secure one end on the towpath and then wrap them around the horse. The loose ends are then passed over pulleys secured on the towpath and get as much help as you can to pull on the ropes. The horse rolls over on his back up the makeshift ramp and on his feet again as he lands on the towpath. I never lost a horse and I had more than one fall in.'

So that was what made Len angry. A bunch of do-gooders off the bank with little or no idea what to do had cost the horse his life and the boatman his source of livelihood. I just hoped that I never became involved in a horse rescue operation.

'What happened to the horse? Did he die?' Oliver asked looking up at me.

'Yes, son, the horse died and was taken away.'

I let Oliver dwell on that fact before I started on the next episode of my tale.

CHAPTER FIVE

I made sure that I spent as little time with Sarah-Anne as possible. For most of the time I was on *John Peel* with Len. I asked questions about this and that and he was pleased to show me how to splice rope, make fenders and decorative rope work. I realised that it was his skill with the rope that made boating easier and I was willing to learn how to tie a boat up and untie it from off the boat and not get the rope wet. I also found bits of brass that he showed me how to make simple decorations for the chimney and how to keep the shine using Brasso and Vaseline. There were lots of small things that I remembered and with practice made them look like second nature.

Then one evening, I remember that it was raining really hard and not a night for venturing out when Sarah-Anne came and knocked on my cabin door before entering. I was not that pleased to see her.

'What do you want?' I asked.

'Josh.'

'That's me.'

She came in closing the cabin doors and pulling the slide across keeping the rain out. She sat down on the side bed.

'Josh, who taught you to read and write?'

'I've no idea. I can't remember. It must have been at my junior school. It's as if I have always been able to read. Why?'

'I just wondered. I had no idea that those stories you read to us were all written down in the bible.'

'Somebody wrote them and put it into English. Why do you ask?'

'Would you teach me?'

'No.'

'Why not? I've shown you how to work on the canal. That's all I know and despite coming off the bank I think that you will make a good boatie.'

'Thank you. It looks as if I never will make a Number One from coming off the bank.'

'I didn't mean that. Ma says that if I asked you nicely you would say 'yes'. Dad wishes that he could read.'

'I've said 'no'. I can't ever see me being a teacher of anything.'

'I already know my letters but don't know how to put them together.'

'I don't think your Pa would like the idea of you coming round here each and every night to learn. He might think that it was only an excuse for me putting my hands on you.'

'No he wouldn't and I wouldn't let you.'

'Sarah-Anne, close the cabin doors when you leave.'

'What is it with you? Why are you suddenly so high and mighty? I had to put up with you when you first came on board. You were mighty humble then so what happened?'

'I got fed up of being put down as 'im off the bank. You were the high and mighty one, not me. I don't have any time for you and that's the honest truth.'

She didn't move but looked down at her hands that she was kneading while resting in her lap.

'I didn't expect you to say 'no'. I didn't realise that I hurt your feelings. I thought that you were just a gawper. We see them all the time and think that they are stupid. I'm sorry that I thought that of you. I can see now that you are anything but.'

I could see that she was filling up and relented.

'Sarah-Anne, if you want to read and I really mean it, you would need to not only learn your letters but work on new words every day and maybe in a year or so you will be able to read parts of the bible.'

'As long as that?'

'It could be longer. The English language is huge with millions of words. I don't know anybody that knows them all. Most of us just know about 15,000.'

'15,000!'

'Sarah-Anne, you already know the words what you don't know is how to write them down or recognise what they say. Now if your dad lets you come each and every evening I will try to teach you but I'm not a teacher.'

'I will have to see what Dad has to say. He doesn't know that I'm here. It was Ma that put me up to it. When are we going to start?'

I put my book down and found some paper and a pencil.

'You need to practice writing the letters. There are two sorts; big and little. The big letters are called capitals or upper case and the little ones; lower case. The big letters are used for all sorts of things at the beginning of names and the start of sentences but before we get to that this is what they look like.'

I then wrote out the alphabet in upper and lower case letters.

'You need to copy those and try to remember the order in which I've put them down.'

'I know the big letters but I don't remember seeing the little ones. What's the difference?'

'None. It's where they come in the sentence.'

'What's a sentence?'

'Not going to prison but it's nothing to concern you right now. You need to remember what the letter look like and tomorrow you can come and show me how many you remember and I will tell you the next stage.'

She looked at the paper and the pencil. It was as if she was afraid they might leap up and bite her hand off. I waited for her to pluck up courage. She did at last pick them up and put them in her jacket pocket. She left without another word. She had more than enough to think about.

That was the start of Sarah-Anne learning to read and write. I intended to give her an English language lesson that would include verbs, nouns and all the other names of words within the sentence but it started with the phonetics followed by the two single letter words 'a' and 'I'. This was then followed by building up the two, three and four letter words before constructing simple sentences. I never considered being a teacher but this was exactly what I was doing. Sarah-Anne was a good student and each and every evening, Saturday excepted, she came and sat with me going through the next phase. It took a year despite her ambition to learn quickly.

This time with Sarah-Anne had an unexpected outcome. Before I arrived at that point I became aware that Oliver was pulling on my hand again.

'Dad, that man.'

Half way down the locks there was a man leaning against the wall. He was scruffily dressed and looked like a down and out. He was wearing an old overcoat and had a trilby pulled down almost hiding his face.

'Dad, that man.'

'What about him?'

'He looks….'

I realised that Oliver was giving me the warning that the man might have serious intent on doing us harm. I was not convinced. As we approached him I gave him a greeting.

'Alright, old son?'

'Ar, ar reckon.'

We were by this time close to him. There wasn't much room for passing on the towpath.

'Yo ah got a light av yer?' he asked.

'Sure.' I said as I searched my jacket pocket for a box of matches. I recognised his local Walsall Black Country accent.

'Yo ay got a cigarette yer cud gi'me av yer?'

I recognised him as being an old boatie. I needed to put a name to the face.

'It looks as if you only have the habit. Here take the packet I said as I took one out for me and lit it. I gave him the rest of the packet and the matches.

'Ar day mean a packet, one wood ha bin OK.'

'Tell me, Slogger, what brings you hanging around here?'

'Ow dun yo know me? Yo'm sort o'familiar but I cor put a naim on yer.'

'You're Archie Perks. You used to bring coal boats from Anglesey for Ernie Thomas.'

'Ah did till that stopped. Ah knows yer but yo need to gi'me a clew.'

'I'm Josh Woodward. Before the war I worked with Len Watson on the *John Peel*. I was called up and spent the next five years walking across North Africa and the best part of Europe. I was with the South Staffordshire Regiment; infantry.'

'Ah've got ya now. Yo woz well educated by all accounts and woz cozy'en up t'Len's daughter, Sarah-Anne.'

'This is my lad, Oliver. I never got close to Sarah-Anne, Len saw to that. I married Oliver's mother and never found out what happened to the Watsons.'

'Adoo, ah kid. Yoer dad woz a real schollard. The Watsons couldn't werk tew boats more or less single honded. Sarah-Anne got knocked up by Eddie Price. They ad a shotgun wedden and 'er ad a kid, a boy. Eddie ad a reserved occupation an werked the boats during the war. Len ad a massive stroke an died. Eddie couldn't werk the tew boats with Mrs Watson 'oo woz getten on an Sarah-Anne 'oo needed tew look after the babby. They sode off the *Rosemary* and went t'live on the bonk someweer in Bentley ah woz tode. Eddie werked the boat single honded on the coal trade.'

'Well, there you are. That's another of my mysteries solved. I'm just taking Oliver to have a look at the Public Wharf. It's a trip down memory lane for me and an education for him.'

'Theer's nuthen to see dahn theer. E'ss all gone t'rack an ruin.'

'Tell me, what do you do, Slogger?'

'Look for werk. Theer's nowt about. What trade the' is on the cut is mainly Caggy over in Oldbury. 'E only cums over ere to teck Joey's t'Moxley tip as duz one o'Matty's blokes.'

I saw his difficulty. He was like most of the boating fraternity he couldn't read or write and was perceived as having no value. There was nothing wrong with his work ethic just his ability to sign his name.

'Slogger, do you know Woodward's leather factory? It's just off Albert Street.'

'Ar, ah noze that. Wor'about et?'

'If you want a job, go there Monday morning about 8

The Tip at Moxley

o'clock. There will be a job waiting for you.'

'Ah dun yo no that?'

'Slogger, I'm Josh Woodward. It's my business. I'm the boss and I've just started you on. Don't let me down but more importantly don't let yourself down.'

'Bloody Hell! What shood ah call thee?'

'What you've always called me, a kid off the bank. See you Monday morning and don't be late.'

I left Slogger smoking my cigarettes sitting on the balance beam of the lock gate. I went back to my walk down memory lane. It was only then did I realise what my father had wanted me to learn – what made people tick and how to deal with people less fortunate than yourself. It was a lesson well learnt.

'Dad, how did you know that man?'

'He worked all his life on the canal and now that the

trade has finished nobody will give him a job.'

'But you did.'

'Oliver, one day the Company will be handed down to you. Taking on people like Slogger will be our salvation. They will repay pay us this simple act of kindness by working hard and being loyal to the Company. Mark my words.'

'That girl that he mentioned, was that the girl you taught to read and write?'

'Yes, it was.'

'How come she was knocked up?'

Now that wasn't a question that I expected from a 10 year old boy. I was unsure how to answer but the facts are the facts and the truth is the truth. I decided to try to explain. 'Well, she had a boyfriend who worked on the boats and he never went in the army. He had what was called a reserved occupation. They got married and she had a little boy. Then as Slogger said, after they were married Eddie worked the boat while she stayed at home with the baby.'

'Did he do her then?'

I had no idea where that came from. My 10 year old son was more worldly wise than I had anticipated.

'Who told you about that?'

'The older boys at school that's all they talk about doing this or that girl.'

'I've no idea what happened with Eddie Price and Sarah-Anne except they were married and she had a baby.'

Oliver was silent as he took in that piece of information.

At the bottom lock I looked across the canal towards the Walsall Public Wharf. It was desolate with sunken boats. There was a notice that I was unable to read. All the buildings were boarded up and obviously empty. They were about to be demolished and the whole area re-developed. I had no idea what the planners were thinking of doing with what was at one time the very heart of the town that gave Walsall its prosperity.

'What are you looking at, Dad?'

'That's where your granddad put me on a canal boat.'

'What did he do that for?'

'I've no idea but it gave me a new outlook on life. Let me tell you more of my story.'

After that first two weeks I went back to find Len and the boats. They were here tied up at the wharf. I had an envelope for Len which was money for my upkeep. After that, my dad would leave an envelope at the wharf office every week and Len could collect it as and when the boats came around.

I was back living on the *John Peel* cleaning the Bolinder engine and polishing the brass until Len collected his orders for the next trip. Over the next four or more years I was on the boat we went to most places on the Brumycham Cut and more than a few other places on the surrounding canals. I hadn't been on the boat long when we had to deliver a load of coal up to the wharf at Welshpool. It meant another trip up the Shroppie and then on to the Ellesmere Canal turning off on the Montgomery. We were just in time getting back to Ellesmere as there was a breach near Welsh Frankton that closed the canal for good. If we had been on the other side of the canal breach, that would have been the end as far as Len and the boats were concerned as there was no way the boats could have been moved around the breach. It was a lucky escape and illustrated how precarious life

Walsall Public Wharf

on the cut could be.

I was getting better with the boats by the day and it was inevitable that one day I would steer the boats. And so it was that I took the tiller of the *John Peel*. Len was distracted by a branch of a tree that had become fixed to the bow of the *Rosemary*. It occasionally happened sometimes on the *John Peel*. While steering the boat you could feel that somehow it didn't respond to any movement required from keeping the boat in a straight line. Somebody, usually me, had to go to the front of the boat, lie on the fore deck and release the branch of a tree or a railway sleeper or whatever the obstruction by using the cabin shaft. In this instance there was the branch of a tree that had attached itself to the bow of *Rosemary*. Len slowed the motor down so that the butty could get closer. I coiled the towing rope as it approached. Getting the towing rope wound around the propeller was not a good idea. As and when the *Rosemary* was close, he handed me the tiller as he used the cabin shaft to move the branch away. I then opened up the Bolinder to start pulling away while easing the towing rope to its full extent. Len got up off his knees and just looked at me. He had nothing to say. I handed the tiller back to him.

'I think that you can have a go at steering for a bit.' was his only comment. I had passed another milestone in becoming a boatman.

It was sometime later that he let me get on with starting the engine and taking the *John Peel* at the start of the day while he saw to casting off. It became easier for Martha. I don't think Sarah-Anne was too pleased but I don't think anything I did ever pleased her. That was her problem and not mine. I loved that engine and over time learnt how to kick start first time every time.

The other notable events were mainly disasters of one form or another. The most traumatic was on a trip to Nechells Power Station. It was a slow journey with more than a few locks, nine at Rushall, thirteen at Perry Barr and five locks at Garrison. We didn't get that far. There was an unusual amount of traffic along the Tame Valley that was added to by the coal trade coming down the Daw End Branch and Rushall Canal. The increased traffic caused a bottle neck at Perry Barr. We joined the line of boats waiting.

Surprisingly there were no boats coming up the flight. Each and every one of the boat crews were busy around the locks being impatient for the boat in front to move as quickly as possible. The Perry Barr Locks were slightly different to the majority of narrow locks in as much as they had ground paddles at the top and bottom gates. Most narrow canal locks had sluices on the bottom double gates. The Perry Barr arrangement would appear to be superior with larger sluices enabling the locks to fill and empty more quickly. Unfortunately, one of the boatmen had stumbled or tripped and fell in the swirling waters as the top paddles had been drawn. He was sucked under and blocked the sluice. There was no hope for him. There was a moment's silence before the shouting by those who saw the accident. Everybody left their boats and ran to the third lock on the flight to help. All boat movement ceased except for the boat in the lower pound that made its way into the next lock. Lock three had to be drained including the upper pound and the lower pound. It seemed as if everything had been well rehearsed as each and every boatman seemed to know what to do and was doing it.

Len put his arm around my shoulders.

'Lad, there's nothing here for you to see. Martha and Sarah-Anne can go to the shops. We shall be here a few days.'

He was right. A few boats at the end of the line turned around to go back and through Birmingham and Farmer's Bridge. It would take at least a day especially if there was extra traffic in Birmingham.

'What's to do?' I asked Len.

'Drain both pounds and hopefully pull him out. It's not a job for the fainthearted.'

Somebody had to go into the sluice chamber and attach a rope to the guy and try to pull him out. It depended where he had become wedged. As Len said it was something that I didn't need to witness. There was a calm quietness around the locks as men jumped in what was left of the water above the top cill.

A policeman arrived as did the Maintenance Gang of the Canal Company. They fixed up sheer legs with a rope

Perry Barr Locks, Tame Valley Canal

and pulley. They managed to get him out and laid on the towpath. His boating days were over. His boat was pushed over on to the far bank until his family could take over.

It was a sad and sobering event. The news would go around the canal community faster than any telegraph. His family would be there the following day everybody giving them the right of way. Any and all the locks would be set and worked for them. The Canal Company men left the site and the locks were refilled with water and we were allowed to proceed. The whole event took three days. It was a warning; more haste less speed and to be forever watchful.

I felt Oliver pull on my arm.

'Dad did you ever fall in the canal?'

'I did quite a bit of sliding around in the snow and ice but there was only one time that I ended up in the canal. I didn't fall in the canal I was pushed.'

'Why?'

'That really is a good question. Let me tell you the circumstances and then you will know.'

It was all to do with Sarah-Anne. I had started teaching her to read and write, as I have already told you. It was becoming a regular thing. One weekend, it was a Saturday afternoon and we had tied up. I went into the local shop to buy a few things when I was confronted by four boys off the canal boats. While I was at school it was alright to wear your school uniform around the town when you were with your friends but out on the housing estates by yourself was a different matter. Meeting one or two boys was not normally a problem but three could be and four definitely spelt trouble. They really enjoyed scragging a kid from the Grammar School. I was always on the look out and I would purposely cross over the road to avoid them. On the tow path I didn't have much choice. They saw me coming and moved to one side away from the edge of the canal. I just knew that there would be trouble as they started calling me names. As I approached, Ed Price, Sarah-Anne's boyfriend was one of them. He was the one that held a grudge against me for spending so much time with his girlfriend. I didn't respond but was on my guard. As I was passing them, Ed, stepped in front of me shouting abuse. I tried to ignore him but he came and pushed me trying to get me into the canal. As he pushed I grabbed the lapels of his jacket and swung him round so that he fell in the water with me on top of him. That was something that we had learnt at school on the rugby pitch. When a boy ran towards you with the ball under one arm while trying to hand you off with the other you still made the tackle by grabbing his arm and turning him around. It didn't matter how big the guy was, it was his own weight that brought him down with you on top of him and not the other way round. It was almost a reflex reaction as far as I was concerned and Ed ended up in the canal with me on top of him.

Canals aren't that deep and this one wasn't. It was no

more than 3ft at the towpath. I stood up and the water was only up to my waist. Ed didn't surface. I reached down and pulled him up. He was half drowned. I pushed him to the edge but couldn't lift him out. I shouted at his friends.

'Stop gawping and pull Ed out.'

They suddenly seemed to become aware of the situation and two of them pulled him out while I lifted myself out of the water. They lay him on his back.

'Not on his back, in the recovery position.'

They didn't know what that was. I turned him over and tried to get as much canal water out of him as I could. I then turned him over and started the life saving routine I had also learnt at school thinking that I would never use it. Little did I realise how useful it would be. After a couple of minutes Ed was breathing again but looking very groggy.

I stood up. 'You need to get him back to the boat and put some dry warm clothes on him. If the drowning didn't get him he might just die of the cold.'

I needed to get back to the boat as fast as I could to find a change of clothes for me.

Back at the boat I quickly undressed and rubbed down with a towel before putting dry clothes on. I hung the wet clothes up in the engine room to dry. I had a visit from Len.

'What were you doing to fall in the cut?' he asked.

'Minding my own business.'

'We'll have less of that. I told your dad that I would look after you.'

'So where were you when I needed you? It was Sarah-Anne's boyfriend, Ed. He took to throwing me in the canal. His problem was I was expecting it and he came in with me. He almost drowned and I've no idea why I resuscitated him. I don't think any of his mates know the first thing about drowning.'

'I need to get over there to sort things out.'

'You do that.'

Len left me to finish getting dressed trying to get warm. I was more than a little bit cold I had the ague setting in and needed a hot mug of tea to help warm me up.

It was some time later that Sarah-Anne came to see me.

'What happened between you and Ed?' she asked.

'You need to ask Ed. He tried to throw me in the canal but came in with me.'

'Yes, I heard and you saved his life.'

'I've no idea why. I didn't owe him any favours.'

'His mates told me all about it.'

'Is he alright now?'

'His mother put him to bed with a hot water bottle and built up the fire in the stove to try to keep him warm.'

'I don't think your dad was too pleased about me 'falling' in the cut.'

'He will get over it. I think that he has an obligation to look after you.'

'I think that I have a vested interest in my welfare as well. You need to come back some other time for your lesson. I'm still shivering.'

'I can see that. I'll see you later.'

I was left alone. I thought that these canal folk were a funny lot.

Before we moved off on Sunday night, Ed came back with Sarah-Anne. I gave him a hard look. I wondered if he would thank me for saving his life. He didn't and in future he wouldn't come anywhere near me.

'And that's how I came to fall in the canal.' I don't know whether it made any impression on Oliver or satisfy his curiosity. I decided to tell him of other events.

'Telling you about falling in reminded me of all the slipping and sliding I did when the winter weather arrived.'

'Did you go out in the snow and ice?'

'In the snow we did.'

It was time relate my winter experiences on the Brumycham cut.

I remember setting off from Gas Street late one afternoon heading towards Tipton and Wolverhampton to pick a load the following morning. Black clouds rolled in and a few flakes of snow started falling. Len was eager to make a start on the journey. I think that he knew bad weather was on the way because he gave me *John Peel* to steer while he was on the butty and the ladies in the cabin keeping warm. He was on cross straps as we ran unloaded.

As we progressed along the New Main Line the wind picked up and it started snowing heavily. In the Smethwick cutting it was blowing a gale and then a blizzard set in. I stoked up the stove and pulled the cabin doors around me. I had my thick jacket on and pulled my hat down as far as I could. I didn't have any gloves and had to use the stove chimney to try to keep my hands warm. I filled the kettle and when the water boiled made a strong cup of tea hoping that would keep me warm. It didn't. The snow piled up down the front of my jacket and on my hat. I could hardly see where I was going. The boats found their own way. At Spon Lane there wasn't the driving wind that we had in the cutting but the snow was still falling and was about four inches deep on the bank.

At the Spon Lane stop I eased the boat into tick over and ran back to ask Len what should we do?

'Caggy has some boats tied up around the corner in Oldbury. Tie up to them for the night and lets see what the morning brings.'

I ran back to the *John Peel* slipping and sliding as I went. Stepping on to the boat counter I nearly fell backwards just managing to hang on to the hand rail on the cabin roof. I needed to go more steadily and watch my step. I put the boat engine into drive and set off to Oldbury.

Sure enough Caggy had some boats moored on the inside and I moved along the line until there were two Joeys close enough for both our boats to tie up to. Len tied up the stern of *Rosemary* and I tied up the front of the butty and the stern end of the *John Peel*. Getting to the front of the motor was difficult and I stepped over the Joey and on to the tow path. It was a safer option that trying to negotiate the gunnel.

Once the boats were secure Len met me on the tow path.

'We can't do any more tonight. Let's see what tomorrow brings.'

With that we both disappeared into our cabins for the night.

It was nice and warm in the cabin and I made sure that the fire in the stove was kept stocked up with coal.

The following morning the weather had relented. It was no longer snowing. The canal wasn't frozen over and after a hot bowl of porridge and mug of tea, Len and I set about sweeping the snow off the boats to continue on our journey. I pitied the horse boatmen that had to follow the horse walking behind him in wet snow and slush.

The other experience was even colder weather over Pelsall Common that always seemed cold even on summer days. There we were caught in the ice. There were no boat movements. I guessed that the ice was about 4 inches thick. Thick enough to be able to walk off the boat to the bank. Together with all the other boats we had to wait for the ice breaker.

You could hear it coming long before it came into sight. The noise of breaking ice was as loud as a clap of thunder. We just cast off our mooring lines as we weren't going anywhere and waited anticipating the ice breakers arrival. Len started the paraffin blow lamp heating up the Bolinder cylinder head.

At last they came in sight. There were four Midland Railway horses pulling the ice breaker. It was a sight to behold. The horses pulled the ice breaker up onto the ice and the rocking of the boat broke up the ice. The rocking was made by men on either side of the boat holding on to a thick wire hawser attached to masts fore and aft on the boat. With four horses pulling they made sure and steady progress along the canal. As soon as they were passed we started the Bolinder engine and were under way hoping that the canal didn't freeze over before we had completed our journey. The ice would come back again that night which meant another wait for the ice breaker again. A thaw in the weather was most welcome.

'Dad, did you do any ice skating on the canal?'

It made me smile. 'No, son, I never did and I can't remember anybody ever trying.'

Tug and Joeys: Winter on the Wyrley & Essington Canal

CHAPTER SIX

Oliver and I were at the Walsall Top Lock. The New Navigation pub was open. That was another trip down memory lane – having a drink in the pub. I took the path off the towpath and went into the pub taking Oliver with me. He was holding on to my hand wondering where we were going.

There was an off licence hatch in the passageway where I could order. The hatch opened and the landlord peered out.

'Half a mild, a packet of crisps and Vimto for the lad.'

The landlord looked from me to Oliver and then back to me. 'We can't have him in the bar just in case but you can come out the back and sit out there.'

'Thanks. Can I have 10 Woodbines as well?'

The drinks and crisps arrived and I took Oliver out the back where there was a bench. I handed the crisps and Vimto to Oliver. I lit a cigarette and tried to remember the last time I was in the New Navigation. I couldn't. My thoughts were still going round the BCN on the *John Peel* and *Rosemary*. I had my audience sitting happily munching on his Smith's crisps and drinking his Vimto. At the age of 10 I think that was more or less all that boys were interested in but he did listen as I related yet another one of reminiscences.

'I need to tell you what happened in Netherton Tunnel on one trip.'

We had a cargo of tubes from Stewart and Lloyds at Coombes Wood. They had a terrific operation going there. They had what I thought were at least a hundred day boats that were loaded and taken to Hawne Basin for transhipment to the Great Western Railway. I have no idea where they took the tube to but we had a trip to Leicester. Len had to scratch his head how he was going to get there it could be along the Grand Union or the alternative would be via Fazeley and then the River Soar. The Grand Union was decided upon. I don't think that Len fancied the river.

Running with no load from Walsall to Coombes Wood was interesting. Above Riders Green there were no locks to negotiate. Netherton Tunnel was fantastic with its two tow paths. It had been gas lit at one time and then electric with a water driven generator at Tunnel End Cottages where the canal passed under the Old Main Line. At the other end of the tunnel the canal was surrounded by ash mounds and coal mines. There were the remains of a chimney and pump house that used to drain the mines. I guessed the water would have topped up the canal. At the Windmill End cross roads we turned left along Dudley Number Two. They had some strange names for the Black Country canals.

It was a pleasant enough trip the canal threading its way between the factories, a few houses and the occasional pub until we came to Gosty Hill Tunnel. Just before the tunnel there was a narrows where we waited. At one time there had been a tug but with less traffic the boat house was still there but without the boat. To my surprise Len started clearing everything off the cabin top, first from *John Peel* and then *Rosemary*.

'What's going on?' I asked.

Len explained. 'This tunnel is not only narrow but it has a low roof. I will put the front light on and have *Rosemary*

Netherton Tunnel

on cross straps. We need to take off the tiller bar and put the engine in drive on tick over. We will eventually come out the other end.'

I wondered how we would steer the boats. The simple answer was that we didn't. We sat in the cabin, lit the lamp and had a cup of tea as we rubbed from side to side in the narrow passage. I could see the roof of the tunnel which at one point was only a few inches above the hatch. This really was a tight squeeze.

Sure enough twenty minutes later we emerged not into open fields but into the middle of a factory. Everywhere was black. There were overhead gantries and steam hissing from various large pipes. This really was the heart of the Black Country. The canal seemed full of boats all of them Joey's. A Joey was normally built of wood and had the same dimensions as a narrowboat but there the similarity ended. The majority were wooden with a few older ones made of wrought iron. They were knows as Bantocks. A

Gosty Hill Tunnel

few had a small cabin at one end. It was not the liveable sort but just for the boatman to have a bench seat and a bottle stove to boil a kettle and to keep the crew warm. The Joeys had a detachable helm that could fit either end of the boat. This meant that they didn't have to be turned around when they reached their destination. They were the mainstay of the coal industry. None of the Joeys had engines all being horse drawn. Here they were being used as a floating warehouse with different size tubes in each. The Company had five tugs about 30 ft in length so that they could turn around in the width of the canal. They were used to ferry the Joeys to and from the interchange basin at Hawne. The factory had its own boat yard where running repairs like re-planking, caulking and blacking could be carried out.

At the dock office we were instructed to go to Hawne Basin turn around and they would be waiting for us. There was no waiting around on this trip. It was only a short distance to Hawne Basin. Beyond that the canal looked overgrown and deserted. The line had been closed some years before with the collapse of a very long canal tunnel at Lappal that required leggers. That was not on our minds as we used the canal basin as a means of turning the boats round.

Back at the factory we were loaded with the tubes from an overhead gantry. We finished loading and sheeted up both boats. We had the tickets signed and we were on our way back through the notorious Gosty Hill Tunnel. I remember I was mightily relieved when I saw daylight at the other end. It was a really slow but steady journey until we arrived at Windmill Junction when there seemed more than a few boats going nowhere. Len shouted asking what the problem was. The problem was that a horse drawn Joey had sunk in the tunnel and nobody could get passed.

'What do we do?' I asked Len.

'It won't be long before they get it up and afloat then we can be on our way.'

'How long will it take?'

'I'm pulling up here for the night and by tomorrow the boat will have been raised.'

'Can I go and have a look?'

'Sure, it will be good experience for you.'

When the boats were tied up in what was becoming quite a line, I set off along to the towpath into the tunnel. The sunken boat was quite some way in. The tunnel was about a mile and a half long so it could have been anywhere. The location of the sunken boat was easy to spot. The men from the boat yard and set up hurricane lamps on both sides of the canal and I went to stand behind one to see what was happening.

Hawne Basin

The sunken Joey was well down. There was little if any trace that it was there. The water level was over the gunnel. There was another Joey that I assumed was alongside the sunken one and there was a portable petrol driven pump filling the floating boat with water. They were sinking the one boat alongside the other! I thought the whole thing madness. When there was only about 6 inches of freeboard on the floating Joey, chains were fastened around the stretchers – those pieces of planking that kept the boat sides rigid. The other ends of the chains were attached to the stretchers on the sunken boat. The men were wearing waders to actually climb on to or into the sunken boat. The pump was then switched around to pump water out the boat they had just filled. I remembered my physics lesson – good old Archimedes – an object displaces its own weight in water. As the one boat was pumped out it raised the sunken boat until the gunnel broke the surface of the canal. A second pump was then deployed to start pumping what water was still in the sunken boat. Not only did they both come to the surface but the discharge from the pumps had the effect of propelling both boats out along the canal. It was slow progress. The sunken boat was full of coal and a halt was made to the pumping. The chains were made secure and both boats bow hauled out of the tunnel.

I asked one of the men where they were going. He didn't know but there were plenty of boat yards around. The nearest one being Harris's yard on the Bumble Hole Arm but they would have to transfer the coal to the other boat first. I was thankful that wasn't one of my jobs.

Next morning we were moving by 5 a.m. with no locks to worry about until we reached Birmingham. Even at that time in the morning there was a short wait at Farmer's Bridge Top Lock and then the double locking down the 13. They were easy enough as they had virtually constant use. That was followed by what was called the 'Quiet Half Hour'. As we turned into the Digbeth branch it looked as if the canal was a dead end with a brick wall facing us. Upon closer investigation I could make out a lock followed by a short tunnel under the building. After the six locks it looked as if the canal met with another dead end but this time there was a junction and a branch to the left. There was just a narrows that could have been a lock at one time. The Toll Keeper came to gauge the boats. This was the Warwick Bar and one of the ways on to the Grand Union.

It was only a short distance to the main line and it wasn't so grand. We came across the 6 locks at Camp Hill. When double locks from Braunston were built they stopped before Camp Hill and we had to bow-haul the loaded butty through. The wharves on the summit level were busy mainly with boats coming up from London. We weren't going that

Windmill End – Cobbs Engine House

far and I never did make the trip to the Metropolis.

At Knowle we encountered the first of the upgraded double locks and progress was improved. It meant a different arrangement for taking the boats through tied together, 'breasted up' as the boatmen would say. The butty and motor were tied together as a one so that only one person was needed to work both boats through the locks. We eased our way down the flight. They had large ground paddles that also speeded up the journey despite having to wind the windlass over 50 times both up and down. What a chore that turned out to be when we hit Hatton Locks all 21 of them.

We tied up at the Cape of Good Hope in Warwick. Len couldn't resist saying 'hello' to Doris who kept the pub and sample the ale. I wasn't far behind him in going in. Doris gave me a look that only pub landladies can which said 'Are you old enough? Working on the canal you may not be but need liquid refreshment'. Evidently the pub had been her family for generations and was one of the old well favoured watering holes. The ale was good.

The following day we pressed on. It was another day of locks in the Warwick countryside. At Braunston we were again at a canal cross roads where the Grand Union and Oxford Canals met. We were on a mission and I had quite a shock at finding a long tunnel having to pass other boats in the dark misty gloom. Beyond the tunnel was Norton Junction just before Buckby locks and then we were on the long and tortuous trip to Leicester; 41 miles and 41 locks, the long Crick Tunnel and the double staircase of locks at Foxton, all locks being single that meant double working. Evidently the money ran out long before the widening scheme of the 1920s got to the Leicester section. It was a long and slow journey.

We had the day in Leicester. I had a look around the City while Len tried to find any sort of load to get us back to Birmingham. If we went back via Coventry there was every likelihood that we could pick up a load of coal from the Griff Colliery into Nechells. He decided to try that.

It was never the same retracing your steps over a route that you had just covered. This was no different except this time we were running light with no load to slow us down. At Braunston we took the Northern Oxford route and yes, we did manage to get two boat loads of coal from Griff. The horse boatmen reckoned they could do the trip in a day. With two boats and long flights of single locks at Atherstone and Curdworth on the Coventry and Fazeley Canals we would be lucky to do it in two.

I had a surprise at the head of the Oxford Canal we passed the Greyhound pub at Sutton Stop. I was put in mind of Maisy and wondered where she was. I hadn't heard from her on the towpath telegraph as it was like to be called. I wondered if we would ever meet up again.

At Nechells, we had the task of unloading the coal on to wheelbarrows and then cleaning the boats getting ready for the next load whatever that might be. It was only a short journey back to the Public Wharf in Walsall where Len collected his money from my father and to get new instructions.

CHAPTER SEVEN

What Len desperately wanted was some sort of continuity of work. It seemed as if we just picked up loads that were urgent and somebody had either failed to turn up or had been laid up due to lack of consistency. That was the case of our next trip, taking fire bricks from the Stourbridge Canal to Stoke-on-Trent where they were re-lining a kiln. We retraced our steps through Netherton Tunnel to Park Head where we turned off the Dudley Number Two canal to the Dudley Number One at Blowers Green Lock. It was a short distance through yet another steel works, Round Oak, where they were using a sort of scoop to dredge the black slimy mud out of the canal It had an aroma that was unique and indescribably awful.

The BCN ended at the bottom of the Delph Locks. Supposedly 9 but I could only count 8. It was another Black Country conundrum. The Stourbridge was rather a strange canal with a feeder coming in from the right as we hit the 16 locks. Where we were loading was some way down. Pearson's brick works were easy to spot and they were waiting for us to get loaded and on our way. Loading bricks was easy enough as the boat trim was uniform.

My story was interrupted again by Oliver. We had left the pub and were back walking along the tow path.

'Dad what's the BCN?'

'The BCN are the initials of the Canal Company; Birmingham Canal Navigation. You will see them on all

Park Head and Blowers Green Lock

Delph 9 Locks

the lock paddles. Some of the boats still have the BCN numbering and if you keep a sharp lookout you might just spot a boundary post marking the perimeter of their land.'

I had no idea whether Oliver understood that but he was then on the lookout for finding BCN initials on all manner of things as we walked along. I went back to my story.

While we were loading I asked Len about the route to Stoke. It was easy enough, carry on down the Stourbridge and after the 4 locks at Stourton turn right on to the Staffordshire and Worcestershire Canal heading north to the Trent and Mersey Canal and then Stone and Stoke. The way he said it I thought that it would be easy. It could have been but having most of the locks spread out and the horse drawn coal traffic going the opposite direction from Hednesford to Stourport Light we had to be vigilant and the double locking was slow. Beyond Calf Heath the traffic was lighter. The Hatherton Branch went off to the right with a lock and then on to Hednesford up to Churchbridge locks. Hednesford would appear to be the centre of coal wharves servicing the Cannock coal field. After that we seemed to have the canal all to ourselves for long periods.

The journey itself was uneventful and it became a regular trip once a month that lasted a couple of years. We never managed a return load. However we picked up a couple of contracts; one was coal from Sideway Colliery to Middlewich and the other to transport aluminium ingots from Ellesmere Port to Wolverhampton. This resulted in a strange arrangement where we went from Stoke to Ellesmere Port via Wheelock, Middlewich and then to Nantwich. It really was a round trip. I saw more of the English countryside and my geography was improved. This lasted for the best part of two years. We then had an enforced stoppage.

The first trip over what is now the Trent and Mersey Canal was almost an education in itself. The potteries were busy with their strange bottle shaped kilns all the way up to Etruria where Wedgwoods had a terrific site. Instead of being back the countryside the canal threaded its way through Shelton Iron and Steel works before entering Harecastle Tunnel. What a trip that turned out to be. There were wooden doors stopping entry. I was told that it was all to do with ventilation the old tunnel was full of methane and not the place to go. We had to wait for the tug to take through all the horse boats with the horses being walked over the top while we tagged on behind.

At the other end of the tunnel the canal water was bright orange in colour. It was from all the iron in the tunnel that made it that colour. We were now in the country but a stop was needed. It was yet another boatman's watering home, The Bird in Hand. It was small and the landlord had to go into the cellar for the beer. It was a drop of good ale.

From there on down through the locks at Wheelock there two locks side by side. I never worked out which were for going up and which were for going down. If the lock was ready, it was used. The only thing I remember from that first trip was squashing a dead dog in one of the locks. It was fly blown and the stench was indescribable. Ugh the thought still fills me with horror.

Middlewich was at the centre of the salt trade and after discharging the coal made a left turn after Kings Lock on to the Middlewich Branch of the Shroppie. We tied up at Barbridge and it felt good to be back on familiar water.

It was some time later that I noticed slowly but surely the *John Peel* was taking on more water each and every day. There had been little or no change in the stern gland but an increase in the depth of water in the bilge. I told Len of this and he took a keen interest and watched as I pumped out the bilge each and every day. We had a leak somewhere. We couldn't see where the water was coming in. The boats needed to be docked without delay to establish the cause of the leak.

It was the first and only time that I saw Len use the telephone. It was in the wharf office where we were loading the ingots. He was calling around the dock yards to see who would accommodate us. He settled on Worsey's yard in Walsall. That was convenient for everybody. We would go there after delivering our present load in Wolverhampton. The leak was getting worse and I pumped out the bilge morning and evening.

The journey from Ellesmere Port to Wolverhampton was just one of many that faded in my memory. The journey from Wolverhampton to Worsey's dock stuck in my mind. We had to have caution going round the double bends of the Wyrley. Devil's Elbow Bridge was aptly named. Not only were there joeys on this section but Ampton Boats that were over 8 ft wide and over 80 ft long taking up to 40 tons. I didn't fancy working one of those around the Wyrley. To get around the sharp bends in the canal the helms were fitted with an attachment to give greater assistance in steering. The boatmen called the added attachment – a 'babbie 'ellum'. The 'Ampton boats were too big for the locks and were only employed on the coal run from Hednesford or Anglesey to 'Ampton Light.

At the boatyard Joe Worsey was waiting for us. We breasted the boats as we approached the yard with *John Peel* dockside. We tied up to other boats alongside the dock. I was puzzled about getting 70ft long narrow boats in and out of the canal which was only 40ft wide at most. The only boat launches I had been witness to were liners on the Clyde where a bottle of champagne was broken over the bow and they slipped silently into the river estuary. There was no way that could happen on the Wyrley and Essington Canal or any other canal on the BCN network. The boats had to be pulled out and launched back into the canal sideways. This I had to see.

Len stepped on to the dock and shook hands with Joe. They had known each other for many years and were well acquainted. I had the job of clearing the back cabin putting everything into the hold of *Rosemary*. Everything would be safe under the canvas but it was everything including the chimney and water buckets. If it wasn't nailed or screwed down it had to be removed. I needed to go and stay back at my parents while *John Peel* was on the dock. It could be a day or a week. Once out of the water Joe would make his pronouncement. Up to that point I would just have to wait.

I was interested to see how they pulled the boats out and asked if I could give them a hand. I think that any help would be appreciated. It started by wrapping chains around the boat, four altogether. The chains were so wrapped that the end put on the winches came from the bottom of the boat rather than the top. Planks were put under boat as the four winches were slowly wound up. The boat keeled over slightly and the planks pushed further under the boat until they were complete under. The winding of the winches continued. Joe put rollers under each plank so that the boat was eased out of the water. I smiled to myself. The rollers were just a telegraph pole sawn into logs about 3ft in length. I wondered how they came by those. The thought passed as more rollers were put under the planks as the boat was eased out of the water on to the bank. This procedure was continued until Joe was satisfied the boat was where he wanted it.

The chains were removed and four jacks used to raise the boat off the planks and rollers until it was about 3ft off the ground. Two of the men off the Dock, Alan and Eddie, carried first one and then another large beams. They were about a foot square in cross section and 8 to 9 ft long. Attached to the beams was what looked like a tree trunk cut in half. I found out these were bostocks. When under the boat, that was secured to the bostocks with pegs, the boat could be rocked from side to side thus giving access to view the bottom. Joe propped up the boat so that it sat square on the dock using a variety of pieces of timber to replace the jacks.

Len joined Joe on the inspection. I followed close behind while Alan and Eddie collected up the planks and rollers for the next time a boat was pulled out. Joe had a pen knife that he went around the boat prodding it as he went. What surprised me that the *John Peel* was of composite construction. That is to say that it was iron on the top and wood below the water line and wooden bottom. This strange arrangement was that the boats have a square cross section they were likely to be worn out along the length of the boat at the corners. It was easier to replace wooden than iron. I wondered if there was a trade off – iron would last longer than wood but more difficult to replace. Evidently somebody somewhere had worked it out. We now had to wait on Joe's pronouncement.

'What do you think, Joe?' asked Len.

'Nothing more than you expected. It needs planks

Narrow Boat on the Dock

replaced at the back end and half a dozen new bottoms otherwise it's lasting well.'

'I'll let you get on. Any chance by the end of the week? You need to have a look at *Rosemary.*'

'It's not a big job and we'll put you ahead of the other work we have on.'

Len went back to the *Rosemary* while I stayed on the dock. There really wasn't anywhere else for me to go.

Alan and Eddie came back armed with mattocks and immediately set about hacking away at the rotten planks at the rear of the boat. I hadn't seen a mattock before and at first thought they were pick axes but having a go myself while they were on their tea break found that the pick end had been changed to an axe. So the mattock had a chisel at one end and an axe at the other. Working on the boat, it was the axe part that was used.

When Alan and Eddie returned they gave me the job of collecting up all the oak splinters that had removed. They were taken to a growing pile of wood ready for burning. They made short work of removing the planks and moved the boat so that they could take out the elm bottoms. I asked what I could do. I was told to scratch brush the iron helm and give it a coat of paint. That was easy enough to do and I was well out of their way.

It gave me the opportunity of seeing what I had been standing on all those months. The round section at the rear of a motor boat was always referred to as the counter. I hadn't given it much thought but seeing it on the dock I realised that the round end was cantilevered off the back of the boat. Under the counter was the propeller. It seemed as if the boat had been built in two halves with one being put on top of the other. Ha! Below the water line the boat shape was a sweep into the propeller while about the water line it kept the shape of the straight sides of the boat.

There was a hole in the counter that a piece of round iron 1¼" or 1½" diameter was passed. The rudder had been attached to this. At the base of the round iron below the rudder it fitted into a cup on the end of a flat piece of iron that extended from the bottom of the boat. This was the skeg. My boating vocabulary was increasing almost by the minute. The top of the round out the Swan's Neck was attached. The Swan's Neck was the round iron about the counter that was in the shape of a 'Z'. On to this was fitted the brass tiller bar that was held in place by an ornamental tiller pin that had come off a poker. Everything below the counter needed to be scratch brushed and painted black.

I had another scratch brush job to do was where the planks had been removed. They had been attached by bolts to the knees of the boat. Those were the iron brackets that held the sides and bottom together. While they were exposed I had cleaned them off and gave them a coat of red oxide. The lads on the yard gave me encouragement until I asked where the black paint was. This was greeted with laughter.

'What's funny?' I asked.

'The black paint as well as all the other paint is on the shelf at Woolworths. You need Len to cough up some ready so that you can go and buy it.'

No wondering they were laughing. I had never seen Len part with any money other than the pocket money my father had given him.

I had a walk into Walsall to buy what paint I thought I needed and went back to see how far the guys had got to repairing the boat. They had been sawing 3 inch thick elm planks to the right size for the bottom of the boat. Now that was a job that I didn't want.

The days progressed. Templates of the oak planks were made and cut to size. They would need to be steamed so that they could be bent to shape. They gave me the job of looking after the steam chest. It was nothing like a chest that I had ever seen before. It was more like a coffin with open ends. It was mounted on two brick pillars so that the chest was well off the ground. Beneath the chest was an old 50 gallon oil drum that I needed to fill with water from the canal. I was given a bucket. Beneath the oil drum was a brazier of sorts. It was a small brick furnace with a chimney at the rear.

Come the day, I was given the task of steaming the planks. They were put inside the chest that was covered over with wet sacking particularly at the open ends. The wooden splinters from the oak planks were placed in the furnace and lit. They would eventually boil the water in the oil drum generating steam that was fed into the chest. My job was to keep the fire burning. The planks would need to be steamed all day and only in the last hour would they be ready.

Joe came to see how everything was going. It was fine. He put his arm around my shoulders to give me his worldly advice.

'Len said that you were a good lad. If you ever get fed up of dragging old boats around the cut you can always come here and I'll find you things to do.'

'Thanks, Mr Worsey but I don't think that I'm cut out for being a boat builder.'

'I'll leave that with you but here's something that you can take away with you. To build a boat you need to burn a boat. I think that you might have just worked that out for yourself.'

I nodded an understanding.

After the 4 o'clock tea break, everything was ready for fitting the steamed planks. It really was every body helping. The sacks on the one end were lifted and the first hot plank removed. It took four men to carry the plank as we ran around the yard to the boat where the plank was offered up and large clamps used to pull the plank into place. The second plank was then fitted. There was nothing more to do until they went cold overnight. They would be secured the following day.

Having fitted the planks and secured them with bolts to the knees, the caulking could begin. Alan and Eddie set about putting in four strands of oakum into each joint. It was another thankless task as they swung their caulking hammers as if they were pendulums on a grand father clock.

They kept me busy with a large can of bitumen that

The Steam Chest

I blacked the side of the boat not with a brush but with a mop and I thought that caulking was another job that I could do without. There was no way that Joe Worsey would get me working on his yard.

At last the boat was ready. It had taken all week and late Friday evening the dock was cleared and two ramps laid from the bostocks to waters edge. Saturday morning was the launch. All the boats were moved along the canal out of the way. The boat was tipped up at and angle towards the canal and held in position with piece of wood set at an angle. The holding pins on the bostocks were removed and there was a short discussion about who would knock out the pin and did anybody want a ride? Sarah-Anne wanted the ride and I was handed a long scaffolding plank.

'What do I do with this?' I asked.

It was Joe that answered. 'Stand dockside underneath the boat and knock the holding pin out of the way and hope for the best.'

What they wanted was somebody to blame if it all went

wrong. I was the fall guy. What the hell? I had nothing to lose. I took up my position.

'Is everybody ready?' I shouted.

There was no reply. With just a short backward lift I swung the plank forward knocking the holding pin away. The boat jolted and slowly started moving gaining speed until it hit the water. It was a perfect launch. There had been no champagne being broken over the bow just me with a scaffolding plank.

I heard shouts from people that had gathered on the towpath on the opposite bank. They had all come to witness the launch but had more than they expected. When the boat it the water it created a tidal wave, a veritable tsunami that had washed over the towpath. The onlookers all now had wet feet hence the shout.

Alan and Eddie pulled the boat back to the bank where Joe went on board to have a look inside. After a few minutes he emerged. He was happy with the work.

The dock closed for the weekend and it was then we started work replacing everything that had been removed. On Sunday, the boats were moved juxta position with everything being removed from the *Rosemary* into the hold of the *John Peel*. The whole process would be repeated the following week.

Caulking

Boat Launch

CHAPTER EIGHT

'Dad, did you ever go back to work for Joe Worsey?'

'No, son, the two weeks there convinced me that there was more to life than repairing canal boats. I had to go home each and every night to sleep and your Nan was none too happy at the state I went home in.'

'Why?'

'I was dirty, covered in rust and then paint and even worse, red oxide and bitumen. I had wood smoke on my clothes and in my hair. For two weeks I couldn't get clean. That was no life for me. The second week was different. Let me explain.'

Sarah-Anne had only ever lived on the boats. That was all that she knew and it came as somewhat of a shock when she was told the *Rosemary* had to be docked and there was nowhere for her to sleep. Martha asked me if it would be possible for her to stay at my parents' house. I could only ask. We had plenty of room to put her up. I had my own room and there were two spare guest bedrooms. When I did ask about Sarah-Anne staying I had a strange response from my mother. I didn't ask my father as he resented anybody encroaching into his space.

'Mom, the canal boats are being docked and there is nowhere for me to sleep while the boats are being repaired.'

'Well, of course, you can stay here at home. It will be nice having you back home. How long will it be for?'

'Only a couple of weeks. The boats are at the boat yard

off the Bloxwich Road. I can go and work at the boat yard each and every day but I need to come home each night.'

'That sounds perfect.'

'Mom, there is something else. For the second week there is nowhere for Sarah-Anne to sleep and Martha, Mrs Watson, has asked if she stay here in the spare room.'

'I don't know about that. You father would likely blow a fuse having a gypsy under his roof.'

'Mom, they aren't gypsies. They are just normal people that have ended up living on boats. That's all they can afford and it's all that they know. They certainly aren't gypsies.'

'I don't know.'

'Mom, I'm going to invite her. This is my house as much as your's or dad's. She will only be here to sleep. She won't want feeding or any looking after. She will come back to the boat yard with me each and every day.'

Mother was somewhat shocked at my statement. It was as if I didn't live there any more.

'I don't know. We will have to see. What's she like, this Sarah-Anne?'

'A pain in my neck. She's 17 going on 18. She's never slept in a bed and never been in a house. It will be as much a shock to her as it will be to you having a grown up daughter living in the house.'

'A daughter! Josh, you aren't...'

'No mother, not in a million years. I don't particularly like her and I can't remember her ever saying a nice thing to me or about me. I've taught her to read and write as she never went to school; come to that, neither did her parents or their parents.'

'That's not what she's like. That's what you think of her.'

'You are probably right. I think that she's a nice girl.

She has a boy friend that she has known for years and everybody thinks that they are made for each other. She is as strong as me and can work the boats by herself. In that sense she's very accomplished where I am definitely not. I don't eat with her or socialise with her. All that we have ever done together is her teaching me how to steer a canal boat and I've taught her to read and write.'

'That still doesn't tell me what she's like.'

'You will just have to make your own mind up. She will come back with me next Sunday.'

So it was settled and I told Martha the following day. Everybody had a week to get used to the idea. I don't think anybody was happy about the arrangement. Everybody had a different reason. I didn't want her there because I didn't particularly like her. Mother didn't want a girl, a young woman coming into her home. Len didn't want to let Sarah-Anne out of his sight. Martha was anxious about letting Sarah-Anne come with me. Lastly, Sarah-Anne was terrified. She had never been off the boat. She had never lived in a house. She had not slept in a bed. Everything would be a totally new life experience for her and she was frightened.

That weekend had been a busy one. I had launched *John Peel*; we had moved the boats around and stripping one boat of every moveable object while returning everything back to the other one. Sarah-Anne had a bundle of all her clothes that she needed to bring with her and at 4 o'clock on Sunday we left the boat yard. It was only a short walk along Carl Street to the Bloxwich Road where we caught the trolley bus into town. Even that was a daunting experience for her. She was terrified at the speed of the bus. It just travelled at a normal speed. There was no racing around Walsall. At the bus yard we had to catch a Midland Red out on to the Lichfield Road and that was another terrifying experience for her.

The whole journey was more than Sarah-Anne had contemplated. Walking up to the house I could see that she was trembling in her boots. She was still wearing boots as they were the only shoes that she possessed. I didn't go in the front door but went round the back to the kitchen door where mother was waiting for us. Father had spent the afternoon at the cricket club. He was President and every Saturday and Sunday afternoon in the season, he graced the cricket ground with his presence. Today was no exception. I did the introductions with my mother.

'Mother, this is Sarah-Anne.'

'Come in, my dear.'

'Thank you.'

'Josh, go and have a bath and get changed. I need to have a chat with Sarah-Anne.'

For once I was pleased to go to the bathroom. I had no idea what their conversation would be like. Did I care? I did not.

After my soak in a warm bath I went back to my room to get dressed for a Sunday evening meal. I shouted downstairs that the bathroom was free. I could hear mother's voice but couldn't make out what she was saying. If it was important I was sure that she would tell me.

Going downstairs I was aware that the house was quiet. Mother was in the kitchen preparing the meal.

'Josh, that girl.'

'What about 'that girl'?

'She's only brought a few clothes with her for the week.'

'Mother, those are all the clothes that she has to her name.'

'And she wears those boots. I've given her a pair of my

house shoes to wear.'

'Mother, she only has one pair of boots. She doesn't have any shoes of any description, well, not to my knowledge.'

'Dear, oh, dear.'

'I think that you are in for a few shocks this week. I don't think she knows how to use a knife and fork and I'm sure that she has never had a meal sitting down at a table.'

'What does she do on the boat?'

'I've no idea. I've never had a meal with her. I always eaten by myself on the other boat. All they gave me was a knife.'

'Dear, oh, dear.'

'While I'm here I will help and she can come with me back to the boat yard each and every day.'

'Dear, oh, dear.'

Mother was in total shock. I went to lay the table in the dining room while mother finished cooking dinner. She took a call from father. He was at a very exciting cricket match between Walsall and Cannock. He would come home when it was over and to keep his dinner warm in the oven. That was just about par for the course with him. The local rivalry between the towns was quite intense at times and evidently this was one of those times. We would eat without him.

Dinner was ready and Mother went to see what was keeping Sarah-Anne. I put out the warmed plates. There would be no starter just a roast beef dinner. I was unsure about pudding. I would find out later.

Mother made an appearance with Sarah-Anne who was dressed in her print frock. She was fresh faced that seemed to be glowing. Under normal circumstances Dad would be offering her a schooner of dry sherry but only having me and Sarah-Anne and no father, mother would have to do without. She was fussing around Sarah-Anne.

'We've put you here.' She was explaining. 'Josh will have to carve the joint and you need to help yourself to vegetables. I hope that you like everything. What you don't like, just leave. It will be alright.'

'Thank you, Mrs Woodward.' were the only words uttered by Sarah-Anne.

I carved the joint and put two slices of meat on to each plate together with a Yorkshire pudding. Sarah-Anne didn't know what to do or how to serve herself. I came to her rescue and gave her two boiled potatoes, a couple of roast, some cauliflower, carrots and peas. I then added some gravy and put it on the table at her place. Mother and I just helped ourselves and joined Sarah-Anne at the table.

We started eating but Sarah-Anne just looked at the plate. She didn't know what to do. I stood up and went to her assistance.

'Sarah-Anne, this is how you use the knife and fork. You stab the meat like this using the fork and then cut it into small pieces like this. You can then stab it again, like this and put it in your mouth. It really is easy. Watch what mom does and copy her if you can.'

I went back to my meal and was finished first. Working out in the open had given me an appetite that was never satisfied with what Martha dished up. I noticed that slowly but surely Sarah-Anne's hunger overcame her embarrassment and ate everything. She was then put out as there was still gravy on her plate. I realised what was missing and went to the kitchen where I cut a slice of bread off the loaf. That's what was missing. I took the bread into her and she used it to mop up the gravy until only the pattern was left on the plate. She looked up and smiled.

Mother collected the plates while I collected the dishes of vegetables. In the kitchen she would make up a meal for father and put it in the oven for when he came back. I then sat with Sarah-Anne at the table.

'Did you enjoy your dinner?' I asked knowing full well that she had.

'Yes, what was it?'

'Roast beef and Yorkshire pudding with onion gravy.'

She was still smiling when mother came back.

'I haven't any pudding and hope that you've had sufficient to eat.'

'Yes, thank you, Mrs Woodward. It was lovely.'

It was mother's turn to smile.

'I can offer you cheese and biscuits or an apple or pear.'

'That's kind but I've had enough thank you.'

'I'm off to my room. I'll have cup of cocoa before I turn in.' I said as I left the ladies to it.

Back in my room, I lay on the bed looking up at the ceiling. Dinner had turned out better than expected. I looked around and found a well read book. The room was that of a school kid. In the couple of years since leaving school and working on the boats, I had changed. I was closer to being a man and not a boy. I had outgrown my prized possessions.

I heard my father's voice and went downstairs to the kitchen to make my cup of cocoa. He looked pleased. Obviously Walsall had won the all important cricket match. He was having his meal at the kitchen table.

'Ah, there you are. Come and sit with me while I eat and tell me what you've been up to.'

I took my drink and sat with him in the kitchen. I told him about working on the dock and repairing the boats.

After this coming week, I would be back working the boats around the canal system. He seemed content with that.

'This girl, you've brought here what about her?'

'She's Len's daughter. He gave me the gypsy's warning about going anywhere near her and I haven't. Her boat is on the dock this coming week and I think that she'll be staying in the spare room.'

'You've not been sniffing around her, have you?'

'Dad, I don't even like her. I don't really want her anywhere near me. On the boats she's on one and I'm on the other. It's the way Len likes it.'

'So do I. I don't want you getting involved with a wench off the cut. Do you understand me?'

'Perfectly. Now I'll bid you goodnight. I need to be at the yard tomorrow by half past seven.'

Dad had finished his meal and pushed his plate away. 'I knew that working on the cut would be good for you. Just stick with it. That's all I ask. Now off to bed with you.'

The following morning I was up at 6, out the door at quarter to seven and waiting for the lads to open the yard gates at half past. It was a week that was a repeat of the previous week but this time it was all new bottoms and a complete new bottom plank. There would be work enough. I had had the practice now it was the real thing.

I started work with the men on the dock fetching and carrying the beams and rollers before working one of the winches to pull *Rosemary* out of the water. Len came to stand next to me. It was a slow and careful process that Joe Worsey made sure everything was right and there would be no mistakes or accidents. Len had something on his mind that was his daughter, Sarah-Anne.

'Where's Sarah-Anne this morning? I expected her to be

here with you.'

'I've no idea. I haven't seen her since dinner last night.'

'You should have brought her.'

'Len, I have no intention of going into her bedroom to wake her up. If she stays in bed; that's where she stays. I'll find out when I get back later.'

'You can tell her that I want her here.'

'Len, I am not going to be the go between you and Sarah-Anne. Go and find her and tell her yourself. Better still you can bring her back here. Now I'm trying to concentrate on getting your boat out of the water and on to the bostocks.'

He walked away, climbed on to one of the boats on the other length to get back to the *John Peel*. He wasn't happy the way I responded to his demands. He came out again later walking around the *Rosemary* with Joe who was prodding away with his pen knife. They then went into a huddle. I guessed Joe was giving Len the bad news. I often wondered how Len paid to have the work done. It was either cash on the nail or some now and again as and when Len could afford it. I never found out.

Martha came and gave me some bread and cheese and a cup of tea at lunch time but really wanted to know how Sarah-Anne had reacted to staying in a house on the bank and sleeping in a real bed. I couldn't help her. I had left before Sarah-Anne had surfaced. I would never know because by the time I arrived back home she would have had a day to come to terms with her surroundings which is exactly what happened.

It was about 6 in the evening when I showed up at the kitchen door. Both Mom and Sarah-Anne were in the kitchen. Mom was preparing the evening meal and Sarah-Anne was helping her. They were bonding as possible friends but with the age difference it was more like mother and daughter.

Mother just took one look at me and issued her instruction. 'Bath now and don't be long. Dinner will be ready in 10 minutes.'

Sarah-Anne just smiled. She had found somebody else that gave me orders that I complied with.

Dinner was just a simple affair compared with the previous day. Dad sat at the table and expected to be served. Mom just dished up a cottage pie, mainly of the leftovers from Sunday. It was nice enough and didn't need a great deal of dissecting so that Sarah-Anne could cope with the meal. Dad was grumpy. It didn't take much to upset his applecart and we bore the brunt of his bad humour.

After dinner I had a chance to find out what happened to Sarah-Anne and also deliver Len's message. It transpired that Mother had taken her to the shops, well not so much of the shops as to the stalls on the market. I had a few gaps in my understanding that needed to be filled in.

'Sarah-Anne, your dad wanted to know why you didn't go to the boat yard with me this morning.'

'I never heard you get up and leave.'

'So what did you do all day?'

'Your mom brought me a cup of tea when your dad had left for work. I then had breakfast and we went shopping around the market. I had no idea that Walsall had such a big market.'

'I thought that you didn't have any money.'

'I didn't and still don't have any. Dad didn't give me any.'

I thought that was about right knowing Len and money. Sarah-Anne pressed on.

'Your mom decided that I needed more things to wear.

She bought me this dress. Do you like it?'

'Yes, very nice. What else did she buy you?'

'Some shoes for the house and some for walking out it. I never knew that there were shoes just to be worn in the house. Wait until I tell mom.'

'I think that your dad will have a few choice words about accepting charity.'

'I don't think that it was charity. It was more like your mom buying me presents.'

I guessed that mom also bought her some underwear and either put what she had to the wash or threw her old clothes away. I had no idea what I would tell Len when I saw him next. I guessed that she would stay at my home for the rest of the week. That turned out to be correct. Len wasn't too happy but Martha resigned herself to being without her daughter for a week. It was one less to look after in the cramped area of the motor back cabin which was smaller than on the butty.

So the week played itself out. I was going to say dragged but it didn't. There was so much work that needed doing to get *Rosemary* back in the water the work was relentless. I took to having my morning and afternoon breaks with Joe, Alan and Eddie in the hovel where tea was served from a kettle that seemed to be permanently on the fire bucket. The brazier burnt pieces of old boat with the smoke just being let out through a hole in the roof. When it rained it put the fire out! I was being accepted as being a part time help when help was needed.

The boat was finished on Friday afternoon and there would be a launch on Saturday morning when the ramps had been put in place. The work had taken longer than the previous week. Sarah-Anne had been conspicuous by her absence. I think Len blamed me for some reason. I had little or nothing to do with her.

Mom had been fussing around all week. It appeared that dad had a cricket club dinner on Friday night and being President of the Club had to put in an appearance at the top table. Along with that he needed to show that he was a family man and his wife and offspring needed to sit alongside him. Mom added Sarah-Anne to the list of his dependants. He wasn't too pleased that he had to pay for an extra ticket but to avoid further conflict – mom had blackmailed him – if Sarah-Anne didn't go nobody would go. He capitulated and agreed.

Now this would be something new for Sarah-Anne; a formal silver service dinner that would go on for at least four courses followed by brandy and cigars for the men. Mom had a mission; how to dress Sarah-Anne. I was fitted up with a penguin suit complete with black bow tie. Sarah-Anne was dressed for the event in a long skirted dress. I had to admit she really did look lovely. Mom had the joy of putting some make-up on her with eye shadow and bright red lipstick. She was hardly the girl that I had taken home the previous Sunday evening with her plaid skirt, sweater and boots.

On Friday evening I arrived back at my usual time and was pushed into the bathroom to get rid of all traces of canal boat from my person. The bitumen on my hands really did take some removing but by 7.30 I was late but ready. We made a handsome group even though I do say so myself. Sarah-Anne and I sat in the back seat of dad's Austin 12 saloon while mom sat with dad up front. At the restaurant where the dinner was being held, dad parked as close to the front door as possible. He looked resplendent with his chain of office around his neck. We were more or less last there and only had time for a quick drink before the meal. This time is was a sweet sherry and being late we took the drinks to the table. We all stood around waiting for the local vicar to say grace. He was an honoury member and had to sing for his free supper.

It was all good humoured as we all sat down to eat. Sarah-Anne was between me and mother so when she was in doubt about something she had somebody to turn to for help. I think that she had arrived on another planet. This was so removed from the fore end cabin that was her little abode that it could have been on another planet. The speeches were tedious when people tried to crack jokes that were both weak and inappropriate. At last, with cigars lit and brandy poured, the bar opened and there was a general free for all.

I met up with some of the kids from my school, indeed from my class.

'What ho, Woody! Where have you been hiding and where did you meet the lovely wench?'

'Hi guys. I've been everywhere and nowhere. Dad put me to work on a canal boat and the lovely wench, as you call her, is Sarah-Anne and she has nothing to do with me I'm glad to say.'

It was Squiffy Mason that picked that last comment up. 'Eh, Woody if you're not interested or in the frame, how about an introduction?'

'What do you need an intro for? Just go and talk to her.'

'Woody, come on now. What happened to the camaraderie spirit?'

'I think it's still in the bottle. Come on then.'

I was pleased in a way as it meant that I could dump her

on to Squiffy and have a beer at the bar with my old mates not having to be her chaperone.

'Sarah-Anne this is Squiffy Mason. What's your first name Squiffy?'

'James.'

'Sarah-Anne this is James. He was in my class at school. He wanted to meet you and now he has.'

Squiffy went into his charm offensive. 'Hello my dear, you look absolutely lovely this evening.'

I didn't hear her reply as I was by that time half way to the bar.

I was on my second drink that mother caught up with me talking to two other classmates from school. She took me by the arm and led me away from them.

'Why have you abandoned Sarah-Anne? She's with that awful Mason boy.'

'Is she? How about that? I never would have thought that Squiffy would have appealed to her but there again who knows the mind of a woman. That one I certainly don't.'

'Josh, she's a lovely girl. You could have done worse that settling for her.'

'Mother, you have no idea of what she's really like.'

'She's more like you. The way you are with each other you are like brother and sister. I would never have believed it.'

Mother's!

I was rescued by my father. 'Josh, my boy, you need to come and press the flesh. It's not what you know but who you know in this world and I need to introduce to a few of the movers and shakers here in Walsall.'

God, this was worse than being with Sarah-Anne. I dutifully went with my father to meet the bank manager, his accountant, the cricket club captain and a few others.

I thought that it was all a waste of time and I was tired. I had been up since 6 that morning and coming up to 11 o'clock at night it was well past my bedtime.

My father entered into a deep business conversation with somebody about supplying leather goods. It was my chance to slip away back to the bar. I had no idea how long it would be before dad had had enough and took us home. At the bar I turned around to be confronted by a lovely looking girl.

'Hello, Josh. I haven't seen you around. Where have you been?'

I had no idea who this girl was. She certainly knew me but I didn't recall ever seeing her before.

'Hello, I've been around and about but nowhere worth mentioning. What about you?'

I was hoping that my throw away line might give me some clue as to who she was.

'I left school a couple of years ago and have gone into nursing. I'm a Student Nurse at the Manor here in Walsall.'

That was no help at all at working out who she was. I had never been to hospital, the Manor or any other come to that.

'You need to remind me what school you went to. I was at the Grammar School until my father thought that they couldn't teach me any more.'

'I know what school you went to. You were in my brother's class.'

'I've just put Squiffy Mason on to the girl my mother brought.'

'Yes, I saw that. Jimmy just loves chasing other bloke's girls. Is she with you?'

So there it was. She was Squiffy's little sister. The last time had seen her she was just straight up and down with not a curve in sight. Now she had blossomed and went in and out in all the right places.

'OK, look I give in. I do remember you but your name escapes me.'

'Ruth. So is that girl with you or not?'

'The answer to that is yes and no. She's been staying at our house for the past week so in one sense she is with my family. As for being with me in the romance stakes, she is definitely not. I don't like her but see her every day. She already has a boyfriend who doesn't like me and the feeling's mutual.'

Ruth's smile became larger. 'While you are at the bar, can you get me a drink, please?'

'My pleasure.'

I bought Ruth another brandy and we found a quiet corner to share the moment together.

'What do you do, Josh? You never said.'

'No, I didn't. I work with Sarah-Anne's father Len, on their canal boats. For the past two weeks they have been on the bank being repaired at Worsey's yard just off the Bloxwich Road. That's why she has been staying with us. I think that Mother is trying to be a matchmaker but is barking up the wrong tree. So tell me about your love life.'

'Ha! Love life, that's a joke. I had been seeing Kenny Willetts until I found that he had been two timing me with Sandra Hepple.'

I started to laugh.

'What's funny?' Ruth asked.

'What an idiot giving you up for that bag of bones, Sandra Hepple.'

'That's his loss not mine. So who have you been seeing?'

'Nobody of any consequence my last girlfriend I've only seen three times in the past two years. Now that's hardly any sort of relationship.'

'Looks as if we are both losers in the love stakes.'

'I don't know. I think things are looking up. Wouldn't you agree?'

She smiled. 'You could be right.'

'What are you doing tomorrow morning about 10 o'clock?'

'I don't know. Tell me what should I be doing?'

'Watching me launch a boat at Worsey's yard.'

'How come you're launching a boat?'

'Somebody has to and it's the job that Joe Worsey has given me. We have to build the launch ramps first and then get the boat in position ready for the launch. I'd like to see you again and that's about the only chance I can think of.'

'I'd like to see you again and all being well you have yourself a date.'

I leaned across and gave her peck on the lips. She really was nice and nothing like the scrawny kid I had known previously.

'Dad, was that you and Mom?'

Oliver had brought me back from my story. I had gone completely away from the canal stories and ended up where I gave my future wife and his mother our first kiss.

'Yes, son that was your mother. A lot happened between then and you coming along as the war intervened but that's another story that I'm not going to tell you.'

'Why not?'

'It's something that haunts me and I can't forget. I don't want to pass that on to you. The canal boat stories are much better as I did see your mom at the launch of the *Rosemary*.

After the Cricket Annual Dinner, I did eventually get back home and went straight to bed I set the alarm for 6 as usual. I guessed that nobody else would be up at that time. I had some porridge and dressed for the boat yard putting on my dark blue overalls. I caught an early bus into Walsall and a Royal Blue Trolley Bus to Carl Street. I was at the yard just after 7.30 when the work men opened the yard gates.

There was an air of anticipation around the yard. I think it always happened when there was a launching. By 8 o'clock the yard was up and running. I helped to carry the planks that made up the two launching ramps while Joe Worsey made sure they were put down in such a way that they wouldn't collapse under a sudden weight of the boat.

The boat was already on the bostocks and was moved into the correct position that was central to the ramps. We were ready. It was time for a cup of tea. I went with Joe, Alan and Eddie into the hovel. When we emerged Len was waiting for me.

'Eh, Josh, where's Sarah-Anne?'

'Back at my house as far as I know. She had a late night last night, well early morning to be precise. I don't think anybody else will be up and about just yet.'

'You should have woken her up and brought her back here.'

'Len, you warned me never to go near her. You need to make up your mind what you want me to do. As far as I'm concerned she's your daughter and you are welcome to her.'

I turned away. There was work to be done and if it wasn't he would be angry about that. This morning, it would appear that there was no pleasing Len Watson.

I had a nice surprise when Ruth came walking into the yard. She smiled when she saw me in my overalls. I smiled when I saw her in a nice summer frock. I went to meet her.

'Hello, Ruth. I wondered whether you would come this morning. We both had late nights and I thought that you might have had a lie in.'

'Morning, Josh. Yes the thought and temptation was there but I think that I wanted to see you again. Last night seemed almost too good to be true.'

'Come and see where we are with the launch. We are more or less ready to go.'

I took her by the arm to the dock side. With the boat on bostocks it appeared larger than it looked when floating on the water. The holding pin was already in place and the canal cleared of boats leaving clear water.

Joe came to me with a scaffolding plank.

'This is down to you, Josh. See if you can make a good job of this one.'

'Thanks, Mr Worsey. I'll do my best.' I said taking the plank.

I turned to Ruth. 'Stand a little way back if you don't mind. You are safe enough but you need to have a good view.'

She moved some way from me as I shouted for the 'all clear' then 'Five, four, three, two, one launch.' I shouted and then swung the plank knocking the holding pin away. The boat lurched and then started sliding off the bostocks on to the ramps and into the canal. It was as near to perfect as didn't matter.

The lads off the yard pulled the boat back so that Joe could have his inspection. We all waited apprehensively.

You never knew with Joe whether it was good or bad. I guess if there was a problem we would haul the boat back out again. He seemed satisfied enough and went into a conversation with Len that I couldn't and didn't want to hear.

I walked around the yard with Ruth showing her various things. She just smiled and took it all in.

'You know, Josh, I've heard of things coming out of the Ark but I had no idea that I would be shown where it was built.'

She had a sense of humour that I liked.

Back at the boats, Len and Martha were moving their bedding and everything else from the *John Peel* on to the *Rosemary*. I guess that Sarah-Anne was out of favour and would have to move her own bedding from the hold of the *John Peel*. That was my next job.

Ruth was perplexed at what was happening. 'Josh, why are they moving things from one boat to another?'

'That's Len and Martha. They live in the back cabin of the boat we've just launched. Sarah-Anne is their daughter and she sleeps in the fore end cabin. When I'm on the boats, I live more or less in the back cabin of *John Peel*. When they have moved everything, I'll take you on board and you can see for yourself.'

To get to the *John Peel* I had to cross over the *Rosemary*. I had no idea what Len's reaction would be for me taking a young lady across his boat. Martha would just smile but Len was a totally unknown quantity. I waited until he was busy in the cabin when I more or less carried Ruth across first the plank on to the *Rosemary* and then on to the counter of the *John Peel*. I sat her out of the way in the cabin which was now devoid of all the Watson's things I needed to transfer mine back again. Ruth was busy looking into all the empty cupboards and draws. My transfer took little or no time as I showed Ruth where I slept. She couldn't believe that I actually lived in such a small space.

I went to see Len.

'What's the plan?' I asked. I guessed that he didn't want to spend another Saturday at Worsey's yard.

'We are loading at Anglesey Monday morning. I need to get round to the Jolly Collier tonight but I've no idea where Sarah-Anne is.'

'Len, we can go round to the Jolly Collier now. I'll go home tonight and bring her back to the boat on Sunday sometime.' I said offering him a solution.

He took a deep breath that was more like a sigh being resigned to a situation he had no control over. 'You do that. We can get going as soon as we get the Bolinder working.'

'Len, you finish off here and I'll start the engine.'

So it was agreed. I went back into the engine room and lit the paraffin blow lamp and waited. It gave me time to explain to Ruth what was happening. She could leave now and catch the bus home or she could come round to the Jolly Collier and I could take her home later. She settled for the boat ride and who wouldn't?

I started the Bolinder with the first swing of the flywheel and after slipping the mooring ropes and putting the cross straps on we were underway. I sat Ruth on the cabin side above the hatch. I could steer the boat and talk to her as we made our way around the Wyrley. We passed other boats tied up at Fishley and had the usual 'Adoo' as we passed as did the boats at Pelsall.

At The Jolly Collier I eased back the engine to put it in reverse to slow down and eventually stop as I removed the cross straps and let the butty drift by. I nudge the butty into the bank as I handed Len the aft mooring rope to tie the boats together. I eased the boats towards the bank where Len jumped off and secured the back of the boats to a mooring ring while I jumped up on to the boards that ran down the length of the *John Peel*. I jumped down on to the fore deck and sorted out the mooring rope, looping it over the T pin on the *Rosemary* before throwing it to Len to secure. I joined him on the bank as we walked back to the cabin.

'Who's the wench you have with you? I've not seen her before.'

'That's Ruth Mason. Her brother was in my class at school. I've known her ages.'

'I'm not impressed that you invited her without asking me first.'

'Len, it was a spur of the moment thing. I'm taking her home now and hope to meet up with Sarah-Anne to find out what she's been up to.'

'I'm not happy about that either.'

'That's something I can't help you with.'

I left Len to rejoin Ruth on the *John Peel*. I found two mugs and made tea. She took it and I think surprised at the unusual flavour. It had been made with condensed milk. We sat in the cabin drinking it.

'I need to get you home. Your parents will wonder what's happened to you.'

'Josh, I've had a lovely time. You are more than I ever bargained for.'

'In what way?'

'The way you launched the boat and just how strong and caring you are towards me.'

'Ruth, I'm hoping to see you again and soon.'

'You haven't left me yet.'

She was right I hadn't. We finished the tea and I rinsed out the cups ready to leave. I locked the cabin doors and then looked at the stride that Ruth would have to make to get across the boats and on to the tow path. I picked her up in my arms. She seemed to be no weight at all and then carried her across the boats. She had her arms around my neck and hung on. When I put her down she still had her arms around my neck and gave me 'thank you' kiss. She really was lovely and I was smitten.

We caught the bus into Walsall and then another bus to where she lived off the Sutton Road. At her front door we stopped.

'When can I see you again?' I asked.

'Later if you like. You can take me to the pictures in town. We can meet up at the Odeon.'

'Now that's a date that I'm not going to miss. I'll see you later.'

It was another two bus journeys to get home to find out what had happened in my absence. It appeared that nothing had happened. Everybody had had a lazy morning. Mom and Sarah-Anne had been round the market shopping while dad had yet another cricket match.

I went and had a lie down and slept for an hour. Tiredness had overtaken me. I got up and had some afternoon tea. Mother quizzed me why I got up so early; where did I go that was so important; why didn't I tell her and so on. I think that Sarah-Anne knew as she asked me about the launch of *Rosemary* and did it

go well. I told her that Ruth had come to the boat yard
and I was seeing her later at the Odeon. She took that
information without comment. I wanted to ask about
her and Squiffy but thought it best if she told me what
she wanted me to know.

I found my jacket and was confronted by mother again.

'Where are you going to now? You haven't been home
five minutes and you are off out again.'

'I'm going to the pictures, if you must know.'

'Oh.'

'I'm seeing Ruth Mason and I don't want to be late.'

What I didn't know was that Squiffy was calling round
for Sarah-Anne to take her out for the evening and we
all ended up going to the Odeon in town. I have no idea
how that came about but it was a great night out for all
of us. At the end of the evening to anybody looking on
would have found it strange that after fond farewells we
departed with each other's partner. I took Sarah-Anne
back to my home. There was little or no conversation as
none was needed.

Sunday was another day where we all met up again.
Squiffy borrowed his father's car and we had a drive to
Cannock Chase where we split up into couples again. I
went walking in one direction with Ruth and Squiffy and
Sarah-Anne in another. In just two days Ruth and I felt
that we had been a couple forever. It was a nice feeling.
We ended up at Squiffy's for Sunday afternoon tea. It
didn't end there as we went to collect Sarah-Anne's things
before going back to the Jolly Collier and the boats.

Len had that strange emotion of being relieved to
see his daughter again yet angry that she had been away
so long. With Squiffy and Ruth with us he said nothing.

I guessed that Sarah-Anne would get his ire when they were alone. I also realised that Martha would pour oil on troubled water and so it was.

CHAPTER NINE

That more or less concluded my story to Oliver. Back home Ruth was still at her W. I. meeting probably helping to clear up. I gave Oliver something to eat. Like all boys of that age you could never fill him up with food. He always wanted more – just like the other Oliver.

I may have stopped relating the story of my time on the canal but my mind was still remembering the subsequent events.

Whenever the boats tied up in or near Walsall we met up with the Masons, as often as not at the Jolly Collier which was one of Len's favourite watering holes. I never found out what Sarah-Anne thought of Squiffy but he was definitely hooked. As for Ruth and I we were happy in each other's company.

All that took a dramatic change. In July 1939, when war was declared both Squiffy and I received our call up papers. I had a sudden departure from going around the canals. Most of the boat people were registered as having reserved occupations not so for me. I wasn't one of the boating fraternity and I went off to Lichfield Garrison of the South Staffordshire Regiment. We were front line infantry.

After the medical it was discovered that I had been in the School Cadets and was well versed in the art of marching and also taking an Enfield rifle to pieces. We hadn't fired real bullets I think the teachers valued their lives giving us guns and ammunition. I was given a commission, second lieutenant that ended up as Captain with field promotions as the war progressed but initially it was an intensive training course for the raw recruits.

It didn't turn out well. The phoney war was soon over and we were deployed in France to help stem the Nazi invasion. We were in total shock as we learnt that Germany had invaded Belgium, a neutral country, and they had surrendered. We were almost surrounded. With what we had left of the battalion we made a hasty retreat to Dunkirk.

Wave after wave of troops were deployed trying to keep the enemy at bay but each line retreated as the next line took over. It was the South Staffs that were the last line. Everybody was surprised and relieved when the flotilla of small boats appeared to take as many troops as they could back to Blighty. I was with my men digging in and throwing everything we had in the direction of the German onslaught.

There were only two or three boats left and we were going to stay to provide covering fire. That was until Squiffy found me and pushed and dragged me into the cascading waves.

'Get on that boat. I'll stay here. You go back and marry Ruth and we will all meet up again in the Jolly Collier. Now go.' He said as he pushed me into the water.

I waded out to the nearest boat and clambered on. I looked back but couldn't see Squiffy. The boat turned around as we made our way back to England through the shells and bullets that were coming our way.

Back in England we had an army of sorts. I was given leave until the Regiment could reform. I found Ruth and we were married. I never mentioned Dunkirk. It was a bitter and terrifying event but not the last. I never saw the Watsons then or since.

After her W. I. fund raising event Ruth returned home full of adrenaline. She had been on high all afternoon selling her cakes for a worthy cause. She asked 'What have you been doing all day?' but didn't wait for an answer as she went to attend to Oliver. He needed a bath and made ready for bed. I went into the kitchen and made a Bolognaise sauce to go with some pasta. Dinner would be simple and easy. That was more or less the extent of my culinary skills.

Ruth came and sat with me after putting Oliver to bed.

'Oliver tells me you went along the canal and you told him about the horse that drowned.'

'I took him on a trip down my memory lane. I shouldn't have told him about the horse but he did ask.'

We finished the meal and cleared the table. Ruth still had the afternoon's event uppermost in her mind. I stopped her as she seemed unable to settle and sit down.

I took her by the arm and pushed her into one of the armchairs in the lounge.

'Ruth, sit down, shut up and listen for just one minute.'

She was shocked into silence at my forceful nature. While I had her attention I retold the story that Slogger had told me about Sarah-Anne.

'Josh, I knew that but never got round to telling you. You came back and married me but there was never a word from Jimmy.'

'I guess you realise that he never made it back from Dunkirk.'

'Yes, I did guess that but you went off again and at

the end of the war you were discharged as being unfit for duty. You were totally wrecked with dysentery and malaria. You have never mentioned any of that but I've nursed you through the nights when you have been shouting and screaming and shivering with fright. I don't know what happened and I don't think you want to remember.'

'I don't want to remember but can't forget and I certainly don't want to tell Oliver. The army not only wrecked my body but scrambled my brain in the process. Today walking along the towpath really helped. I have now closed the door on the war and my time on the canal.'

Ruth looked down at her hands resting in her lap. 'I've always thought that you and Sarah-Anne were meant for each other. I thought that she only went with Jimmy to be near you. You two were so close and almost inseparable.'

'I never saw it like that. We lived together working the boats. She wanted to marry Ed Price, have a pair of boats and be Number Ones. I just wanted an easy life and learnt all the tricks that the boaties used. I don't know where Squiffy fitted into all of that. At that Cricket Club Annual Dinner I stole a kiss from you. I had never been that bold before. At Dunkirk it was Jimmy that pushed me into one of the last boats while he stayed behind. I think that he had fallen for Sarah-Anne but couldn't separate her from her lifestyle. He told me to leave him there, come back, marry you and we would all meet up again at the Jolly Collier knowing full well that would never happened. From that first kiss it has been you and only you and nobody else. Maybe I should tell you that I love you more often than I do.'

'Josh Woodward, this might come as a big surprise

Sunset at Walsall

to you but I fell in love with that young man launching a canal boat who carried me on and off the boats. You would always be there for me and protect me. Everybody respected you. I desperately wanted your love. Whether you realise it or not I loved that kid off the bank and still do and I've been waiting all these years to get you back again. At last, I hope that you have closed all the doors on your previous life to start again with me.'

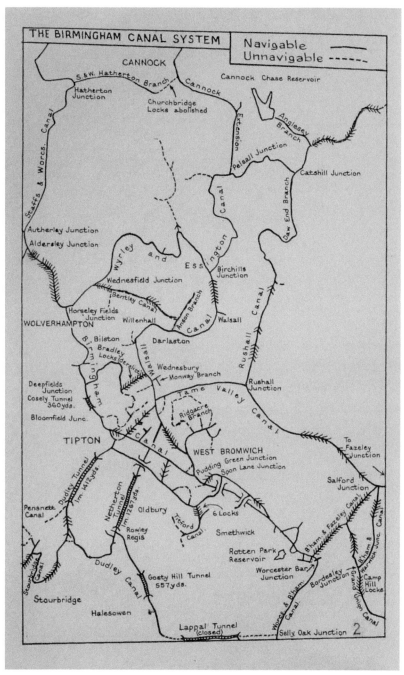

Map of the BCN Canals